Margaret Th

Tea Rooms
of Britain

Published by
Whitehill Publishing
7 Bournemouth Road
Chandlers Ford
Eastleigh
Hampshire

© Whitehill Publishing April 1995

ISBN 0 9525838 0 1

Research: Karen White

Cover Design: Claire Zillwood

Printed by: Peter Cansfield Associates Ltd

My grateful thanks to the following
for their invaluable assistance:-

Helen Eade
Mike Hamilton
Dennis Hovell
Anna Punshon
Karen White

and especially to

Kelly Richards

without who's inspiration this book
would not have been possible.

M.T.

CONTENTS

ENGLAND

SCOTLAND

WALES

TEA, A POEM

While Bards renown'd dine Feat of Arms rehearse
No hostile deeds prophane my milder Verse
From boisterous Ward my Lays entirely free,
The sweet resistless Force of gentle tea.

Thy Power rever'd o'er num'rous Realms is known
and half the willing world appears thine own
In China fix'd thy throne, her sons renown'd
In Arts adore thee and thy worth resound
Glad Europe's fair Daughters catch the flying Fame
and raise a thousand Alters to thy Name!
Thy gifts they taste, and while they taste they prise
Nor envy Jove the Nectar of the skies!

(Aaron Ward)

ENGLAND

*I could have introduced you to some
very beautiful people. Mrs Langtry and Lady Lonsdale
and a lot of clever beings who were at tea with me.*

(Oscar Wilde - letter to Harold Boulton 1879)

The Canary Restaurant

3 Queen Street   Disabled Access
Bath   Parking 100m.
01225 424846

Established for over fifty years, and run by the Davis family for the last twenty six, The Canary Restaurant can be found nestling beneath Trim Bridge in one of Bath's earliest cobbled streets, where Jane Austen reputedly bought her hats.

With few exceptions all the cakes and pastries are prepared on site, using good quality, additive free ingredients. The clotted cream tea comes with wholemeal scones and a loose leaf tea and includes a selection of sandwiches. There is also a strawberry cream tea, and on Saturdays the Anniversary Tea features speciality eclairs, mille feuille and French fancies. The Canary offers a range of special blends of exotic and fruit teas, with a Tea of the Week.

Cherry Tree Gifts and Tea Rooms

4&5 Pulteney Bridge   Disabled Access
Bath   Parking 100m.
01225 447364

Situated in the middle of the world famous Pulteney Bridge and overlooking the River Avon, with marvellous views across Bath, the Cherry Tree Gifts and Tea Rooms is a family business run by Diana and Graham Towers, who aim to welcome visitors to the historical City of Bath.

West country cream teas are one of their many specialities, with a pot of tea, homemade scones, clotted cream and jam. Also available are a wide range of buns, pastries, flans and tarts - all baked locally.

Teas on offer are Assam, Darjeeling and Earl Grey, as well as a selection of herbal and scented teas and various coffees and soft drinks.

Lilliput Teashop

1A North Parade   Disabled Access
Bath   Parking 50m.
01225 466437

Adjacent to the Abbey Compass Hotel, this typical tea shop is within easy reach of the Roman Baths, the Pump Room, the Abbey and the Crescents and gardens for which the city is famous.

Run by Harry Hurst, the venue serves clotted cream teas and Bath buns. Scones are made locally, as are the teacakes and the shortbread fingers. There is also a choice of ice creams.

The teas in the pot are Ceylon, China or Earl Grey and a variety of soft drinks and hot beverages accompany the food. Last orders fifteen minutes before closing time every day.

BRISTOL

Brackenwood Tea Rooms

131 Nore Road   Disabled Access
Portishead   Parking on site
Bristol
01179 818199

With superb views of the Welsh hills across the Severn estuary, Brackenwood Gardens are listed among the English Tourist Board attractions. Visitors can enjoy a vast range of rare trees and shrubs, as well as pools, ponds, a bog garden and a waterfront enclosure. The tea rooms are on site and can be found on the lower coast road between the golf course and Fedden village.

With a choice of seating inside or on the terrace, guests can enjoy a broad selection of various homemade goodies. Proprietor Anne Quarterman recommends the homemade cakes, scones and apple and cinnamon pie in particular. The range of teas include Ceylon, Earl Grey and various fruit teas.

Closed: Last 2 weeks in January.

Mortimer's Coffee House and Parlour
Unit 14 Broadwalk Shopping Centre   Disabled Access
Knowle   Parking 100m.
Bristol
01179 772077

Situated in the shopping centre near to Somerfield's supermarket, Mortimer's is a soothing oasis where guests can enjoy an hour of olde worlde hospitality. Afternoon tea can be enjoyed on the tivoli watching the world go by, or in the comfort of the parlour where newspapers are readily available.
Old Fashioned Afternoon Tea comprises a pot of the tea of your choice, together with egg and cress sandwich and a fresh fruit scone with jam and cream. The choice of tea is wide: Assam, Ceylon, China, Darjeeling and Earl Grey all feature. Bread, cakes, scones and jams are all home baked.

Closed: Sundays.

WESTON-SUPER-MARE

Pickwicks Tea Shop
41 Meadow Street   Disabled Access
Weston-Super-Mare   Parking 50m.
01934 644796

Well established now since its opening in 1980, Pickwicks Tea Shop offers a genuine welcome from proprietor Colin Richards and plenty of atmosphere with its olde worlde decor. Five minutes from the town centre and featuring the museum as a local attraction it is well-situated to provide a value for money tea all year round.
In summer the menu comprises a clotted cream tea with scones, jam and a pot of tea, while the rest of the year offers, for example, a Danish pastry or crumpets with tea or coffee. Among the teas available are Earl Grey and Darjeeling.

Closed: Sundays.

BEDFORD

The Strawberry Tree

3 Radwell Road
Milton Ernest
Nr. Bedford
01234 823633

Disabled Access
Parking on site

The founder member of the Guild of Tea Shops, The Strawberry Tree is a two hundred year old thatched cottage, situated in the centre of the village. The interior is just as attractive, with tea served on Royal Doulton Finebone China and linen and lace tablecloths.

John and Wendy Bona are the proprietors, who aim to provide their customers with food prepared in their own kitchen, using the best of ingredients. As they are Egon Ronay Recommended, this is no idle boast.

A set afternoon tea includes a selection of sandwiches, a scone with clotted cream and homemade strawberry preserve, along with a pot of tea. Desserts are homemade and include individual fresh strawberry tart. The selection of loose leaf teas includes Assam, Ceylon, China, Earl Grey and Darjeeling, plus a more exotic assortment.

Closed: Mondays, Tuesdays and all of January.

-------0-------

There is a great deal of poetry and fine sentiment in a chest of tea.

(Emerson)

Tea Cosy Catering

Dinton Pastures Country Park   Disabled Access
Davis Street   Parking on site
Hurst
Nr. Reading
01734 321071

Situated in a country park with walks around lakes and gravel pits, Tea Cosy Catering will appeal to its many visitors. There is a children's play area for families, and the surrounding countryside is famous for its birdlife. Cream Teas are realistically priced, or there is tea and cake. Cakes and scones are home baked and the teas available include China, Darjeeling and Earl Grey.

KINTBURY

Miss Muffets Tea Rooms and Craft Shop

2 Church Street   Parking on site
Kintbury
01488 657100

Located in the picturesque village of Kintbury, just off the main street, half a mile from the River Kennet and close to the local railway station, Miss Muffets Tea Rooms and Craft Shop can be found above the Butcher's shop, Thatchers, in the village square. Beautiful countryside surrounds this lovely village, which is popular with walkers and cyclists.

Proprietors Julia Radbourne and Christine Wynn have tried to bring back the typical tea shop atmosphere in the decor and ambience of the tea rooms. Clotted cream teas come with a choice of two homemade preserves and a pot of tea or cup of coffee. Most food is cooked on the premises, and in addition to the cream teas there is an assortment of cakes, jams and scones. Teas include favourites such as Assam, Ceylon, Darjeeling and Earl Grey.

Eton Tea Rooms
64 High Street   Disabled Access
Eton   Parking 100m.
Windsor
01753 861003

Close to the River Thames and with good views of Windsor Castle, the Eton Tea Rooms are close to the Eton Bridge and within easy reach of Eton College, the College gardens and local antique shops.
Proprietor Andreas Stavrinides offers a variety of homemade cakes, scones and jams, and the teas available are Assam, China, Earl Grey and Darjeeling.

*Wouldn't it be dreadful to live in a
country where they didn't serve tea?*

(Noel Coward)

Waddesdon Manor "Stables Tearoom"

Waddesdon Manor   Disabled Access
Waddesdon   Parking on site
Aylesbury
01296 651282

Established in 1957, the Stables Tearoom shares the Rothschild Family Home with the "Old Kitchen" Restaurant of Waddesdon Manor. The Manor houses the Rothschild collection, and in the tea room itself is the Old Carriage Horse sculpture from the Rothschild collection. The Head of Catering offers a cream tea, with scones, jam, cream and a pot of tea. There is a choice of cakes and sandwiches. Assam, Ceylon, China, Earl Grey and Darjeeling are amongst the speciality, herbal and fruit teas. All food is made on the premises, including the bread, and the meat and eggs used are organic.

Closed: Mondays (except Bank Holidays), Tuesdays.

BEACONSFIELD

The Old Tea House

7 Windsor End   Parking on site
Beaconsfield
01494 676273

Set opposite the Church in the picturesque old town of Beaconsfield, The Old Tea House is a Grade I Listed building, with internal brick exposed walls and a Tudor facade. It enjoys views of the Church and church yard.
On offer is an excellent selection of home baked cakes, shortbread and tea cake, along with a choice of Cornish clotted cream teas. The smaller appetite is also catered for. Speciality teas include Earl Grey, Assam, Darjeeling, Lapsang and Afternoon, or Columbian Coffee and a wide range of soft drinks are available for visitors who want something different.

Closed: Mondays (except Bank Holidays).

CHALFONT ST GILES   **Buckinghamshire**

Teatime
4A The High Street   Parking 50m.
Chalfont St. Giles
01494 871099

Teatime is located on the village green, in a pretty village setting, not far
from the National Trust cottage where the poet John Milton lived.
Visitors are welcomed with a choice of menu.
The Traditional tea comprises two scones with whipped cream, preserve
and a pot of tea, while the Village Tea includes sandwiches and a choice of
either scones with cream and jam, or a cake with a pot of tea.
Scones and cakes are home made and the range of teas include Assam, Earl
Grey and Darjeeling.

CHALFONT ST PETER

The Myrtle Tree
8 Market Place   Disabled Access
Chalfont St. Peter   Parking 50m.
01753 885371

Run by the local Baptist Church and staffed by volunteers, The Myrtle Tree
lies opposite Budgens supermarket. The cream tea and various homemade
cakes and scones are temptingly priced and Earl Grey is the speciality tea
on offer.

Closed: Thursday afternoons, and Christmas week.

HIGH WYCOMBE   **Buckinghamshire**

The Coffee Shop
Jardinerie Garden Centre   Disabled Access
Studley Green   Parking on site
High Wycombe
01494 485965

Located in a garden centre close to West Wycombe village and House, The Coffee Shop is surrounded by good walking countryside.
Proprietor Christine Smith offers a light, bright plant-filled room, with a courtyard setting in the summer.
In addition to home made cakes and scones, teas such as Assam, Darjeeling and Earl Grey are served.

MARLOW

Burgers of Marlow
The Causeway   Disabled Access
Marlow   Parking 100m.
01628 483389

Set in an eighteenth century building at the bottom of Marlow High Street and close to both the Bridge and the Church, Burgers of Marlow boasts wood block flooring and air conditioning. There is open access from the tea room to the chocolate shop and bakery.
The tea room is run by the Burger family, who offer a well priced menu for their cream tea. A pot of Yorkshire blend tea is served with homemade scones, whipped cream, preserve and a cake from the selection table. Bread and cakes are also home made, and types of tea include Assam, Ceylon, China, Earl Grey and Darjeeling. A wide range of soft drinks and hot beverages are available.

Closed: Sundays and Bank Holidays.

MARLOW   **Buckinghamshire**

The Compleat Angler Hotel
Marlow Bridge   Disabled Access
Marlow   Parking on site
01628 484444

The Compleat Angler is an English Country House, 350 years old, and named after Izaak Walton's famous book on fishing. Situated on the River Thames, it is within walking distance of Marlow.

To complement the scenic views, every effort has been made by Heritage Forte to enhance the atmosphere, with crisp white linens, sparkling silverware, bone china and comfortable Lloyd Loom Furniture.

Guests at teatime are provided with a selection of finger sandwiches, including smoked salmon. There are homemade cakes, pastries and scones with Devon clotted cream, and a choice of 18 teas or coffee.

WINSLOW

Jennie Wren's Tea Rooms
23 Market Square   Parking 50m.
Winslow
01296 715499

Housed in a listed building in the main market square, Jennie Wren's Tea Rooms are close to Winslow Hall, reputed to have been built by Christopher Wren. The proprietor, Jennifer Nilsen, is pleased to welcome guests to tables that are old treadle sewing machine bases, with hand-embroidered tablecloths. Concessions to 20th century life include solar panels for hot water and winning the W.I. Best Ladies' Loo in Buckinghamshire award, 1994. There is a private dining room available for up to sixteen people.

Afternoon tea comprises assorted sandwiches, scone, cream, homemade preserve, a pot of tea or coffee and is competitively priced. Farmhouse Tea substitutes two fried eggs on toast for the sandwiches. Assam, Ceylon, China, Earl Grey and Darjeeling teas are available.

Closed: Mondays.

CAMBRIDGE   Cambridgeshire

Aunties Tea Shop
1 St. Mary's Passage   Disabled Access
Cambridge
01223 315641

Established in 1979, Aunties Tea Shop overlooks Gt. St. Mary's Church and the Senate House. The building is historic, decorated in Victorian style, with lace tablecloths, waitress service and tables outside in the summer. Proprietor Yvonne Prevett offers Aunties Special Cream Tea, which includes egg and cress sandwich, scones, jam and cream and a pot of tea .
Also available are the mouthwatering home made specialities, hot banana cake with butterscotch sauce and cream, and gingerbread served hot with maple syrup and cream. To wash it all down, the selection of teas, includes Assam, Ceylon, China, Darjeeling and Earl Grey.

The Orchard
45 Mill Way   Disabled Access
Grantchester   Parking on site
Cambridge
01223 845788

The Orchard is something of an institution. Since 1897 people have walked, rode or punted from Cambridge to have tea. Near to the river, the Meadows, Wantchester village and its church, the tea rooms, too, are an attraction. Rupert Brooke, the poet, wrote the famous line, "Is there honey still for tea?" as a direct reference to Orchard House, where he lived in around 1909.
The Orchard Tea Pavilion has recently been restored for the winter. In summer guests sit in old deck chairs outside. Staff dress as Edwardians all year round to give the impression of being caught in time.
Cream teas start with The Ten-to-Three Special! In winter Cinnamon Tea provides a warmer alternative to Assam, Ceylon, China, Darjeeling and Earl Grey. Many other teas are served with the home made fare.

Ely Cathedral Refectory

Chapter House   Disabled Access
The College   Parking 50m.
Ely
01353 667735 Ext. 246

The Refectory is situated at the west end of the cathedral next to the shop. The cathedral is the obvious place of interest, but Oliver Cromwell's House, Ely Museum, river walks and the Sports Centre are all local for the visitor.
Friendly staff serve in a cheerful and attractive environment. There is room for endless options when choosing tea, with a variety of home made cakes. Among these are gateaux and cheesecakes, teacakes, scones, treacle tart and speciality Cathedral bread pudding. There is a choice of tea, including Earl Grey and Darjeeling.

KIMBOLTON

The Tea Room

9 East Street   Disabled Access
Kimbolton   Parking 50m.
01480 860415

The Tea Room is a Mediaeval Hall house situated on the east side of Kimbolton, not far from the Castle where Catherine of Aragon was confined and died in 1536. Inside, low wooden beams complement the lace tablecloths and bone china. Cakes are displayed in the Welsh dressers. In the summer there is seating outside in the courtyard where there is always a shaded spot if guests prefer. Traditional Cream Tea offers two scones with cream and jam and a choice of tea, coffee or a soft drink. Strawberry Cream Tea and Gateau Cream Tea also tempt the hungry visitor. Cakes and scones are home baked and there is a good variety of teas including Assam, Ceylon, China, Darjeeling and Earl Grey.

Closed: Mondays, and mid-December to mid-January.

SAWSTON   Cambridgeshire

Compass Point Tea Room
69 High Street   Disabled Access
Sawston   Parking 100m.
Cambridge
01223 576039

The Tea Room was set up last year by the Compass Trust Charity, to provide work experience for adults with learning difficulties. Next to North's Bakers and near to the War Memorial, the Tea Room is set in a village, which is reflected in the decor. The interior is finished in white pine and the paintwork is in rustic colours. One of the tables has an inlaid chess and draughts board on the surface.

A very friendly atmosphere accompanies the serving of various teas. There is no set menu, but a range of cakes, buns and teacakes to enjoy with tea or coffee.

Closed: Saturday afternoons, all Bank Holidays, and the Christmas period.

-------0-------

Stands the Church clock at ten to three?
And is there honey still for tea?

(Rupert Brooke 1887-1915)

Hatties Limited
5 Rufus Court   Disabled Access
Northgate Street
Chester
01244 345173

Set in a cobbled roadway opposite the Bluebell pub, Hatties offers outside seating during the summer months, with attractions such as juggling and craft markets in the Courtyard at weekends.

The tea shop is furnished traditionally with wooden chairs, old embroidered tablecloths, music to match the period feel, and emphasis on good and friendly service.

Afternoon tea consists of sandwiches made from thickly sliced granary bread with various fillings, a large home made Hatties scone with butter, jam and cream, a choice of cake and a pot of tea. Bread is baked locally and the cakes are home made and generously sliced. Assam, Ceylon, Darjeeling and Earl Grey are among the teas with which to finish the repast.

Closed: Sundays.

CONGLETON

Astbury Tea Shop
Astbury Marsh   Disabled Access
Congleton   Parking on site
01260 277099

Located within a couple of minutes walk of the historic village of Astbury and five minutes drive of Congleton, Astbury Tea Shop is ideally situated for cyclists and walkers.

Cream teas provide a sandwich with a choice of filling, a scone, jam and cream and tea or coffee. Cakes, scones and some jams are home made, and the home baked specialities include fruit pies with a variety of fillings, gateaux and lemon meringue pie. To quench the thirst are a choice of teas, including China and Earl Grey.

Closed: Mondays to Fridays between October and March.

DISLEY
Cheshire

The Cottage Tea Rooms
7 Market Street
Disley
01663 764259

Parking 100m.

One of a row of cottages dating from 1824, The Cottage Tea Rooms is on three floors, the first opening onto a terrace. The tables are made from old treadle sewing machines, decorated with fresh flowers and lace tablecloths, old photograph prints hang on the wall, and country magazines and books of local interest are available to read.

Tea is served on white Wedgewood Insignia, with Cheshire Tea comprising two scones, jam, cream, two slices of fruit cake with Cheshire cheese and a pot of tea. Afternoon Tea provides an assortment of dainty sandwiches, cream cakes, a choice of two homebaked cakes and a pot of tea. Darjeeling, Earl Grey and various herbal teas are available, with P.G. Tips for the less adventurous.

Closed: Mondays and Christmas week.

FRODSHAM

The Cottage Tea Shop
121 Main Street
Frodsham
01928 733673

Disabled Access
Parking 50m.

Set in the town centre near to the Castle Park Arts Centre, the old building has a low, beamed ceiling. Lace tablecloths, bone china and lots of fresh flowers give a traditional ambience. Children are welcome, with colouring books, high chairs and training cups available on request. The toilet facilities are spotless.

Cream Tea consists of a freshly baked scone, jam, cream and tea or coffee. Afternoon Tea offers a choice of sandwich, a scone with the trimmings and a slice of cake. Cakes, scones and jams are home baked and the teas on offer include Assam, Darjeeling and Earl Grey.

Closed: Wednesdays and Sundays.

Dorothy's Tea Shoppe
72 Chestergate   Parking 100m.
Macclesfield
01625 503733

Situated above Gate House Antiques, Dorothy's Tea Shoppe is part of an old beamed building. It is not far from the Heritage Centre with the Silk Museum and various old schools and churches.

Dorothy herself is the proprietor, presenting tea to her guests on Eternal Beau tea service. Very reasonably priced, Cream Tea offers a home baked scone with jam, cream and tea. There is a choice of other home made produce: lemon meringue pie, carrot cake and Bakewell tart, and Earl Grey is the speciality tea. Guests can purchase a cloth made "Dorothy" bag as a souvenir of their visit.

Closed: Wednesdays and Sundays.

Gawsworth Hall Tearoom
Gawsworth   Parking on site
Macclesfield
01260 223414

Set in the car park area of the historic country house, Gawsworth Hall Tearoom has magnificent views front and rear, and several interesting features of its own, such as the large staircase and Victorian chandeliers. Food is served on white china by waitress service only.

There is plenty of room for children to play outside, and in Summer meals can be served al fresco.

Cheshire Tea consists of two home made scones with jam and cream, a slice of home made fruit cake and a pot of tea, which can be filled with Assam, Ceylon, China, Darjeeling or Earl Grey Tea.

Closed: From October to the week before Easter.

Blueberries Speciality Tearoom and Cafe
2 Post Office Place   Disabled Access
Albion Road   Parking 50m.
Northwich
01606 331992

Set behind the public library and opposite Sainsbury's, with salt mines and
museums as local attractions, Blueberries has been highly commended for
Restaurant of the Year by Vale Royal Borough Council and is a Gold Award
winner for customer satisfaction.
Its relaxing surroundings make it a haven of peace as guests enjoy the waitress
service, background music, a healthy eating menu and a quiet position.
Afternoon Tea is a scone with jam and fresh cream and a pot of tea. There is a
choice of twelve loose leaf teas, including Assam, Ceylon, China, Darjeeling
and Earl Grey or ten ground coffees served by the cup or cafetiere.

Closed: Sundays.

-------*0*-------

Tea! thou soft, thou sober, sage and venerable liquid...
thou female tongue-running, smile-smoothing, heart-opening,
wink-tippling
cordial, to whose glorious insipidity I owe the happiest moment of
my life, let me fall prostrate.

(Colley Cibber - The Lady's Last Stake)

The Georgian House
58 High Street
Yarm
01462 785653

Situated in the historic town of Yarm, near the town hall and close to the river development, The Georgian House is on the first and third floors and covers three rooms, with a small shop in a fourth.

Decorated in Georgian style with white china and silver teapots the ambience is that of a typical Georgian town house, the traditionally clad waiting service reinforcing that impression.

All food is home made from scratch, using traditional Yorkshire recipes. A typically Yorkshire High Tea offers home baked ham with tomato chutney and crusty bread or a granary roll. Jams are made from a local farm and there is a good range of cakes for the delectation of guests.

Closed: Sundays.

-------0-------

Now stir the fire and close the shutters fast,
Let fall the curtains, wheel the sofa round,
And, while the bubbling and loud hissing urn
Throws up a steamy column, and the cups,
That cheer but not inebriate, wait on each,
So let us welcome peaceful evening in.

(William Cowper)

BOSCASTLE   Cornwall

Carpenters Kitchen

The Harbour   Disabled Access
Boscastle   Parking 100m.
01840 250595

Built in local Cornish stone on the site of the old carpenters workshop from
the days when the village was part of the Manor estate, Carpenters Kitchen
is located in the natural harbour of a picturesque village. Inside, the walls
display old photographs, and in winter there is a coal fire. Tea is served on
a matching tea service and includes scones or cornish splits with a pot of
loose leaf tea, allowing a choice of special House Blend, Assam, Darjeeling,
Earl Grey or Lapsang, along with a variety of fruit infusions.
All cakes are baked on the premises and local crabs are collected from Port
Isaac. Other specialities include meringue deserts and ice creams.

CRANTOCK

Cosy Nook Tea Gardens and Restaurant

Langurroc Road
Crantock
Nr. Newquay
01637 830327

Local to Crantock Beach and St. Andrew's Well, Cosy Nook Tea Gardens
are situated in the heart of Crantock village and have been a family run
business for 15 years.
Established before 1900, pictures of old Crantock and the Tea Gardens in
1918 can be compared with the present. A high rail displays teapots. Outside are trestle tables with lace tablecloths and deck chairs.
Cornish Cream Tea comprises two home made scones, jam and cream and
a pot of Earl Grey tea. Owners Andrew and Nicola Keast offer delicacies
like almond slice, eccles cake, fudge cake and various sponges, all baked
by their mother.

Closed: November to Easter

"Crumbs"
38 Fore Street   Parking 50m.
Fowey
01726 833603/832652

Next to the main Post Office in Fowey, "Crumbs" is in a prime spot for various coastal walks and near to the scenic harbour which offers sailing and yachting. An artist works on the premises and the area is shared with an art gallery and gift shop selling original art and prints, greeting cards and music.
Cream Tea offers a pot of tea, two scones (plain or fruit), strawberry jam and clotted cream. Scones, cakes and pasties are baked on site and the other speciality is local farmhouse ice cream. Vegetarians are catered for and a No Smoking room is available. Teas include Assam, Darjeeling, Earl Grey and various herbal infusions.

LAUNCESTON

Windmill Patchwork & Cafe
23 Westgate Street   Parking 100m.
Launceston
01566 775076

Local to Launceston Castle and the steam railway, the cafe is part of a Victorian shop. The tea garden is set beside the steep hillside garden, which can be viewed from certain tables in the cafe.
The decor inside the cafe follows a Laura Ashley theme, with fresh flowers on the tables throughout the year, and as guests eat they may make friends with one of the many teddy bears on display. The shop stocks Caithness glass, teddies, candles, patchwork and fabrics.
The Cornish Cream Tea furnishes the hungry visitor with two home made scones, jam, cream and a pot of tea. Home bakes include the speciality crispy fruit crumble and coffee cream sponge. Popular teas are Assam and Earl Grey.

Closed: Sundays.

The Windmill Tea Room
Cold Northcott Wind Farm   Disabled Access
St. Clether   Parking on site
Launceston
01566 86276

The Tea Room is situated in the middle of England's largest windfarm, amidst rugged Cornish countryside, with scenic views of Bodmin Moor. Visitors will be interested to see Trediddon Trail, Trethorne Leisure Park and the St. Clether Church and holy well. A shop area sells local crafts and items related to the environment and adjacent to the tea rooms is the visitor centre.
Cornish Cream Tea comprises two scones with jam, cream and a pot of tea. There is also a selection of cakes, biscuits and bread pudding. Bread, cakes, scones and jams are all home made and the cream is produced locally. Speciality tea is Earl Grey.

Closed: October to April 1st.

MARAZION

Gilly's Tearoom
Market Place   Parking 50m.
Marazion
01736 710327

The tea room is in the centre of Marazion, opposite All Saints' Church. Nearby Marazion Marsh is a haven for birdwatching visitors. Inside, tablecloths and aprons complement the china-ware and on sunny days it is possible to sit at the tables in front of the building where flower baskets make a pretty sight.
The proprietors are the Hiscocks who aim is to give value for money with fast and friendly service. Scones and cakes are all home baked, with a choice of specialities like banana cake, carrot cake and chocolate fudge cake. A range of herbal teas and old favourites Assam, Ceylon, China, Darjeeling and Earl Grey are served.

Closed: End of October to March.

The Sail Loft Restaurant

St. Michael's Mount   Disabled Access
Marazion
01736 710748

Set on the west side of the harbour at St. Michael's Mount, with parking on the mainland, The Sail Loft is a converted boat store and sail loft, with good views over the harbour and Mounts Bay.

Tea is served on unique crockery featuring the family crest of the St. Aubyns who live at the castle. Cornish Cream Tea consists of a pot of National Trust tea with home made splits or scones, strawberry preserve or honey and cornish clotted cream. Also available is the local cornish dairy ice cream, as well as a range of home baked bread, cakes and biscuits using locally produced ingredients.

Closed: 1st November to 31st March or Good Friday.

MORWENSTOW

Rectory Farm Tea Rooms

Rectory Farm   Disabled Access
Morwenstow   Parking 50m.
01288 331251

Situated opposite the ancient Church of John the Baptist, Rectory Farm Tea Rooms are only 500 yards from some of the most spectacular cliffs of North Cornwall with a coastal footpath leading to a cliff walk.

The farmhouse tea room dates from 1296 when it was owned by Somerset monks and is furnished with high-back settles and antique tables. There is also an area which sells locally made arts and crafts.

Tea serves two large home made scones, local Cornish clotted cream, jam and a pot of the tea of your choice. Among these are Ceylon, China and Earl Grey. Cakes are home made as well, with specialities such as rich chocolate, carrot, banana and cherry.

Closed: End of October to week before Easter.

The Old Pilchard Press
Old Quay Street   Disabled Access
Mousehole   Parking 50m.
Nr. Penzance
01736 781154

Set off the quay in the old part of the traditional fishing village and near to the birds' hospital, The Old Pilchard Press was converted from an old fish store and is made from local granite, with two foot thick walls.

Cornish Cream Tea is served at round tables in china teapots, with matching water jugs and consists of two scones, strawberry jam and clotted cream with a pot of tea or coffee. Specialities include large tea cakes, carrot cake and ice creams like Knickerbocker Glories. Cakes and scones are home baked and China, Darjeeling and Earl Grey are served along with a selection of herbal teas.

Closed: End October to March.

Pam's Pantry
3 Mill Lane   Disabled Access
Mousehole   Parking 300m.
Nr. Penzance
01736 731532

Established in 1965, Pam's Pantry is just past the Lobster Pot Hotel on the main road through the village of Mousehole, a picturesque fishing village, with views over Mount's Bay and St. Michael's Mount. Heather Boase is the current proprietor, who has kept the original style of the tea rooms. The historic building is also home to a well-known art gallery and a quality gift shop.

Cornish Cream Teas furnish the hungry guest with home made scones, a selection of jams and clotted cream, as well as a pot of tea. Or there is a choice of luscious cakes: fresh cream Cornish Meringue, or vanilla, mocha or lemon cakes. Teas include Darjeeling and Earl Grey.

Closed: November to February.

The Old Loft
Porthallow Cove   Disabled Access
Porthallow   Parking on site
Nr. Helston
01326 280782 / 280063

Situated right on the beach, adjacent to the Five Pilchards public house, The Old Loft is handy for the local cove and walks.
Proprietor Ann Bastable boasts peace and tranquility for her guests, wonderful views and service with a real smile.
Various combinations make up the cream tea of your choice, with cakes, scones and jam all home baked. The teas include Assam, Ceylon, China, Darjeeling and Earl Grey and a service charge is included in the price.

Closed: End of October to Easter.

PERRANPORTH

Beach Tea Rooms
4 Beach Road   Parking opposite
Perranporth
01872 572117

Three miles from Golden Beach, Beach Tea Rooms are owned by Neil and Patricia Wild. Summer visitors are welcomed to sheltered tea gardens which boast an ornamental fish pond and an aviary with tropical birds.
A Cream Tea consists of a pot of tea for one, along with two home made scones, strawberry jam and Cornish clotted cream. Among the teas on offer are Ceylon, Darjeeling and Earl Grey.

Closed: October to March.

POLPERRO   Cornwall

Piskies Pantry
Pridmouth House   Disabled Access
Landaviddy Lane
Polperro
01503 72614

Set in the village centre close to the historical fishing harbour and the heritage centre, Piskies Pantry has been owned by the same family for sixteen
years.
Denyse and Barry Taylor welcome visitors to the Grade II listed building,
which has a wishing well and wall paintings as distinguishing features.
The Pantry serves various menus, including cream teas. All bread, scones
and cakes are baked on the premises, and there is a good selection of teas,
including Assam, Ceylon, China, Darjeeling and Earl Grey.

Closed: November to Easter.

The Plantation Cafe
The Coombes   Disabled Access
Polperro   Parking 100m.
01503 72223

Maurice and Ann Vaughan are justly proud of their tea shop, it having featured
on local radio, television, and even in a Japanese magazine.
Inside, dark beams and white walls complement wheelback chairs, willow
pattern tea service and a copper hood over the fireplace. It was a founder
member of the Guild of Tea Shops, and has won awards for its gardens.
Cornish Cream Tea comprises scones, strawberry jam, Cornish clotted cream
and a pot of tea. Scones, cakes and jams are home made and fresh strawberries
are available in season. Teas include fruit and herbal varieties, Assam, Ceylon,
China, Darjeeling and Earl Grey.

Closed: Saturdays, and November to Easter.

The Singing Kettle
7 Fore Street   Parking 100m.
Polruan
Nr. Fowey
01726 870334

A short distance up the main street from the harbour, The Singing Kettle is set in the quaint village of Polruan on the estuary of the River Fowey close to spectacular cliff walks. Tea is served on bone china, and service is old fashioned and cheerful. On fine days tea is served in the partly walled cottage garden. Cornish Crab Tea, comprises crab sandwich, garnished with salad, a scone with jam and cream - or home made cake and a pot of tea. The Singing Kettle Tea offers cucumber sandwich with home made cake and a choice of Assam, China, Darjeeling, Earl Grey or Herbal tea in the pot. Bread is made at the bakery across the road.

Closed: Limited opening between November and March.

PORTHTOWAN

Avalon Tea Room
Echo Corner   Disabled Access
Coast Road   Parking on site
Porthtowan
01209 89075

Opposite the garage at the bottom of the hill and close to Sandy Beach, which is ideal for surfing, Avalon Tea Room has excellent sea views and is in a Mining Heritage area.
Guests are welcomed by the comfortable atmosphere and friendly service provided by the owners, Ann and Terry Luckwell.
Cream Tea includes two scones or Cornish splits, jam, clotted cream and a pot of tea or cup of coffee. There is a wide selection of home and locally baked cakes, scones and even pickles, and teas include Earl Grey.

Closed: Tuesdays (except in August)

Bumbles Tea Room

Digey Square   Disabled Access
St. Ives   Parking 100m.
01736 797977

Set near an artists' community, the Tate Gallery and local beaches, Bumbles Tea Room is just fifty yards from the town centre.
Jerry Drew is the proprietor, who welcomes you to an olde worlde tea room, located in old St. Ives. Cornish Cream Tea consists of two home made scones with strawberry jam, clotted cream and a pot of tea or coffee. Ten varieties of tea are on offer, including Assam, Ceylon, China, Darjeeling and Earl Grey.

Closed: Sundays in winter season.

TRURO

Cherry Garden Tea Room

Carnon Down Garden Centre
Carnon Down
Truro
01872 865937

Situated in one of Cornwall's main garden centres, four miles from Truro City Centre, the Cherry Tree Garden Tea Room is close to the National Trust Garden at Trelissick, the River Fal Estuary and the Cornish coast.
At the rear of the detached premises is a lawned garden available to customers for dining when the weather permits.
The full Cornish Cream Tea offered by the proprietors, William and Carol Spurway, consists of two home made scones (plain or fruit), with Cornish clotted cream, strawberry jam and tea for one. All the bread and cakes are also home baked. Among the teas on offer are Assam, Ceylon, Darjeeling and Earl Grey.

Closed: Easter Sunday and Christmas.

AMBLESIDE   Cumbria

Chester's Coffee Shop
Kirkstone Galleries   Parking on site
Skelwith Bridge
Ambleside
01539 432553

Set within the Kirkstone Galleries, Chester's Coffee Shop is named after a rather old, extremely stubborn and particularly unattractive English Bull Terrier, nonetheless beloved by proprietors Stephanie Barton and Karen Lawrence.

There is no set tea menu, but a variety of cakes and scones are baked on the premises, using only good quality ingredients. Among some of the most tempting goodies are the Westmorland crunchie, fudgy peanut slice and lemon yoghurt cake. Lakeland special brew is the native tea, with Ceylon, China, Darjeeling and Earl Grey joined by herbal teas.

MELMERBY

The Village Bakery
Melmerby   Disabled Access
Nr. Penrith   Parking on site
01768 881515

The 200 year old building overlooks the village green and houses a craft gallery displaying local crafts. Proprietor Andrew Whitley has created a relaxed, friendly atmosphere which caters for all occasions and the needs of walkers, cyclists and families alike. There is a special, chip-free children's menu, and the ingredients used throughout the bakery are organically grown, most of them on the attached smallholding.

Bread, cakes, scones and jams are all baked in the wood-fired brick oven. Village Bakery Cream Tea offers freshly baked wholemeal bread and butter, a brown scone with jam and cream, a selection of cakes and a choice of tea from Ceylon, China, Darjeeling and Earl Grey, along with a variety of caffeine-free tisanes.

Closed: Restricted opening in January and February.

ALSTONEFIELD   **Derbyshire**

Post Office Tearooms
Alstonefield   Disabled Access
Nr. Ashbourne   Parking on site

In the centre of Alstonefield, are the Post Office Tearooms, next to the village shop and post office. Two cosy tea rooms lead off the passage, complete with old beams, wonderful antiques and brasses. Proprietors Jean and Ernest Allen reckon the guest who can match up all the old chinaware on display deserves a prize!

Cream Tea is served with two home made scones, a dish of cream, jam and a pot of tea or coffee. The Dovedale Tea serves the pot of tea or coffee with local Hartington Stilton cheese, home made fruit cake, celery and fresh fruit. All cakes and scones are home baked, with Bakewell and treacle tarts both firm favourites. Among the teas available are Assam, Ceylon, China, Darjeeling and Earl Grey.

Closed: Wednesdays, Thursdays, and mid November to mid March.

BASLOW

Goose Green Tea Rooms
Nether End   Disabled Access
Baslow   Parking 50m.
01246 583000

Goose Green Tea Rooms overlooks Baslow's Goose Green with attractions including Chatsworth House and Park.

The tea rooms live up to their name with the predominantly green decor and the selection of goosey gifts. Large picture windows let guests watch the world go by, after which walks can be taken over the famous Gritstone Edges. With a No Smoking policy, proprietors John and Margaret Smith pride themselves on a clean environment and friendly service. There is an extensive range of home made fare, with speciality banana and poppy seed cake, cream-topped carrot cake and butter shortcake. Teas include Assam, Ceylon, Darjeeling and Earl Grey.

Closed: Fridays.

Hilary Beth's Tea Room
1 Laburnum Market Place   Disabled Access
Castleton   Parking 50m.
Nr. Sheffield
01433 620397

Situated in the market place of a small village in the Derbyshire Peak District, Hilary Beth's Tea Room is not far from the Blue John Caverns. The tea room is very old, with oak beams, stone walls and a black and white ceramic tiled floor. The furnishings are Victorian and include lace tablecloths and curtains, china cups and saucers and tables made from old sewing machine trestles with glass tops.

Reasonable prices mean that a very pleasant repast can be made on scones, jam, cream and tea. All cakes and scones are home baked and among the teas available are Assam, Darjeeling and Earl Grey.

EYAM

Eyam Tea Rooms
The Square   Parking on site
Eyam
01433 631274

Eyam, known as "Queen of the Peak" and "Plague Village" has a rich history dating from at least 1500 B.C. when its stone circle was erected. As well as Roman relics there is also a fine example of a Celtic Cross and the stone houses of the village where the Plague destroyed nearly 80% of the population in the 1600s. The Tea Rooms themselves are set in the village square.

Eyam Cream Tea comprises two fluffy scones served with whipped cream and strawberry jam, with a pot of tea or a "bottomless" cup of coffee. Fruitcake Tea is served with Wensleydale cheese and whole Chinese walnuts, not to mention the cake. Cakes and scones are home made and there is a vast selection of teas, including Assam, Ceylon, China, Darjeeling and Earl Grey.

Closed: Mondays, and October to Easter.

MELBOURNE   **Derbyshire**

Melbourne Hall Tea Rooms
Blackwell Lane   Disabled Access
Melbourne   Parking 100m.
01332 864224

Located in the grounds of Melbourne Hall, near to St. Michael's Church, the tea rooms are close to the craft centre and the lake. Built about 1710, the premises were originally the wash house/bakehouse of the Hall, and had their own courtyard, which today is used for patrons in fine weather.

Tea comprises assorted sandwiches, scones and jam, various cakes and a pot of tea, or the simpler tea of two scones with jam, cream and a pot of tea. Cakes and scones are home made and the teas available include Ceylon and Earl Grey.

Closed: Mondays (except Bank Holidays), Mondays, Wednesdays, Thursdays and Fridays during January and February.

-------0-------

Mushroom Sandwiches (for ten)

Stew ten mushrooms with black pepper, lemon juice and salt, two red chillies, one egg and one gill of milk. Add two large tomatoes, half an ounce of breadcrumbs, half an onion and mash together.

(Five O' Clock Tea, 1886)

OVER HADDON   **Derbyshire**

Courtyard Tearoom
Lathkill Dale Craft Centre   Disabled Access
Over Haddon   Parking on site
Nr. Bakewell
01629 815058

Part of the craft centre, there is plenty to see as well as eat, with a book-binder, clock restorer and potter on site. The floral arrangements and paintings on sale, tables with seersucker tablecloths and pretty pink and white china combine to create a traditional atmosphere.
Afternoon Tea provides a choice of sandwiches with side salad, cake from a wide selection, a scone with jam and cream and a pot of tea or coffee. Cakes and scones are home made and favourites are toffee walnut tart, Bakewell pudding and lemon slice. Locally made ice creams are also on the menu. Teas include Darjeeling and Earl Grey, with a range of flavoured mineral waters from nearby Wildboarclough.

Closed: Early January to mid-February Monday to Friday.

REPTON

Brook Farm Tea Rooms
Brook Farm   Disabled Access
Repton   Parking on site
01283 702215

Brook Farm Tea Rooms have a brookside location in an old barn. A large private garden provides play equipment and easy access for the disabled. Waitress service by a polite and cheerful staff make it easy to see why this venue is Egon Ronay recommended and a founder member of the Tea Council and Guild of Tea Shops.
Farmhouse Tea gives a choice of freshly cut sandwiches, a home made scone with butter and jam and a pot of tea. Brook Farm Tea offers two home made scones with butter, jam and cream with a pot of tea. Cakes and scones are home made and teas include Assam, Darjeeling and Earl Grey. The locally made ice cream boasts many unusual flavours.

RIDGEWAY   Derbyshire

Kent House Country Kitchen
Ridgeway Craft Centre   Disabled Access
Main Road   Parking on site
Ridgeway
Nr. Sheffield
01742 473739

Opposite "The Swan" public house, the Kent House Country Kitchen is
minutes away from various walks along the Moss Valley. While the tea room
is situated within the old farmhouse, the craft centre is on the premises of
the old Kent House Farm.
Cakes and scones are home made and the teas available include China and
Earl Grey.

Closed: Mondays (except Bank Holidays).

YOULGREAVE

Meadow Cottage Tea-Room
Holywell Lane   Disabled Access
Youlgreave   Parking 100m.
Nr. Bakewell
01629 636523

The building is two hundred years old with beautiful views overlooking the
River Bradford and Bradford Dale. There is an original Hovis sign outside.
Inside, the fresh flowers, lace curtains, log fire and antique fittings contribute
to the memorable atmosphere. A quarry tiled floor means that hikers are more
than welcome, and the tea room is visited by walkers from around the world.
As well as cream teas, there is a variety of cakes, which, with the scones are
home made. Bakewell tart, walnut flan, orange cake and date slice all feature
and there are many more to choose from. Darjeeling and Earl Grey feature
along with six other speciality teas.

Closed: Mondays (except Bank Holidays).

ATHERINGTON   **Devon**

The Village Shoppe and Tea Room
The Square   Parking on site
Atherington
Nr. Umberleigh
01769 560248

The Village Shoppe and Tea Room is a fifteenth century building with wooden beams and inglenook fireplace, set in a pretty Devon village opposite Atherington Parish Church.

Cream Tea furnishes hungry guests with two scones, cream, jam and a pot of tea. Devon Tea adds a sandwich and cake. Cakes and scones are home baked and the home made fudge is a speciality. Earl Grey is the main tea on offer.

Closed: Mondays (except Bank Holidays and school summer holidays).

BOVEY TRACEY

The Old Cottage Tea Shop
20 Fore Street
Bovey Tracey
01626 833430

The Old Cottage Tea Shop was established during the 1950s. A traditional olde worlde cottage, it has beams and a Devon stone fireplace. Tea is served on bone china tableware and it has been a winner of Britain in Bloom for its window boxes and hanging baskets.

Devon Cream Tea provides two scones, jam and clotted cream and a pot of tea. Afternoon Tea offers a choice of egg and cress or cucumber sandwich, a scone with jam and clotted cream and a choice of cake.

There are four types of scone and these, along with cakes and jam are all home made, using fresh local ingredients. Other specialities include fruit pies and mousses, clotted cream meringues and locally made ice cream. Among the teas are Assam, Ceylon, China, Darjeeling and Earl Grey.

Closed: First two weeks in October.

BOVEY TRACEY Devon

"Pink's Place"
Courtenay House   Disabled Access
76 Fore Street
Bovey Tracey
01626 835363

Mentioned in the Bovey Guide, Courtenay House has an historical background, at one time being a "Mission House" for nuns. It is close to Becky Falls and Dartmoor. With gardens front and back, the proprietor, Christine Richardson, has created a homely atmosphere full of period charm, with old tableware and linen tablecloths with lace and embroidery, antiques and bric-a-brac.
Cream Teas comprise two scones (fruit or plain) with jams and clotted cream from the farm, along with a choice of tea or coffee. Afternoon tea adds a choice of sandwich and a slice of cake. All scones, cakes and jams are home made and among the teas are a choice of Assam, China, Darjeeling and Earl Grey.

CHAGFORD

The Old Forge Tea Rooms
6 The Square   Disabled Access
Chagford   Parking 50m.
01647 433226

Formerly the village forge, the Tea Rooms were established in the 1930s and enjoy an international reputation and clientele. They are next to the National Westminster Bank. Chagford is a bustling, ancient stannary town with historic buildings and fascinating shops.
Tea is served on English china and the Devonshire cream tea includes two scones, two jams, clotted cream and a pot of tea or mug of coffee. The Old Forge Savoury Break offers a cheese scone, two hot potato cakes, butter and the same choice of beverage. Cakes and scones are home made and there is a wide range of teas, including Assam, Ceylon, China, Darjeeling and Earl Grey.

Closed: Wednesdays during winter season, and 3 weeks in November.

CLAWTON   **Devon**

Court Barn Country House Hotel

Clawton   Disabled Access
Nr. Holsworthy   Parking on site
01409 271209

Standing next to Clawton's 12th century church, Court Barn was rebuilt in 1853 from a sixteenth century manor house and stands in five acres of gardens. The house is full of antiques and paintings and one dining room overlooks the croquet pitch, used in Summer. A member of the Guild of Tea Shops, it is also Egon Ronay recommended.

Bread, scones, cakes and jams are all home baked, Devon Cream Tea providing scones, jam and cream with a pot of tea, and the Court Barn Special Tea comprising cucumber sandwiches, cake and meringues. A mouthwatering selection of cakes include Marsala and almond cake, honey and cherry and chocolate and walnut. There are 45 different teas available.

Closed: First two weeks in January.

DARTMOUTH

The Spinning Wheel

Hauley Road   Disabled Access
Dartmouth   Parking 50m.
01803 832766 / 832645

Located next to the hospital just off the quay, The Spinning Wheel is a thirteenth century building, with three ghosts! The sunny courtyard has an abundance of flowers and the front of the building is covered in Virginia Creeper and ivy. Proprietors Shaun and Rosemary Pound keep their guests from fading away with their Devon cream tea, which consists of two scones, jam and clotted cream, washed down with an unlimited supply of loose leaf tea. The Devon Farmhouse Tea adds a free range boiled egg and toast and a piece of cake. Cakes and scones are all home baked and among the teas on offer are Assam, Ceylon and Earl Grey. All in all a very pleasant haunt.

Closed: Mondays in winter.

DAWLISH   Devon

Muffins Tearooms

Hughenden House   Parking 100m.
5 Queen Street
Dawlish
01626 864989

This character tea room, winner of a Good Cream Tea Guide Award, is situated
in a pretty seaside town, near the brook that is home to the famous black
swans. Proprietor Susan Buckley serves tea on attractive china tableware and
asks her guests not to smoke.

Devon Cream Tea comprises a pot of tea, two scones (plain, fruit or wholemeal),
a selection of jam and thick clotted cream. Muffins High Tea offers a choice
of Welsh Rarebit and other toppings on toast with a choice of cake and a pot of
tea. Specialities include home baked crumpets, meringues, spicy muffins and
sugar free cakes and jam in season. Herb teas are accompanied by a selection
of traditional teas such as Assam, Ceylon, China, Darjeeling and Earl Grey.

Closed: Wednesdays in summer - Sundays as well in winter.

HATHERLEIGH

Acorns Tearooms

12 Bridge Street   Disabled Access
Hatherleigh   Parking 50m.
01837 810479

Set on the main street next to the newsagent, Acorns has many places of
interest nearby, including the church, the local pottery, and the pretty white
stone cottages.

Inside, the proprietor Angela Nixon is pleased to offer teas in an eighteenth
century atmosphere where the exposed beams give a cottage effect. Cream
teas include two large home made scones with jam, clotted cream and tea,
and the speciality tea is Earl Grey.

Closed: Wednesdays in summer; Saturday afternoons and Sundays as well
in winter.

HAWKCHURCH   **Devon**

Fairwater Head Hotel

Hawkchurch   Disabled Access

01297 678349   Parking on site

Established in 1972, the Fairwater Head Hotel can be found off the B3165
Lyme Regis to Crewkerne road. Hawkchurch is known as the "village of
roses" and the gardens of the hotel have won the Ashley catering award for
the "Best Ten Hotel Gardens".

The Edwardian country house overlooks the Axe Valley, and rather than a
set menu offers a choice of home baked cakes, biscuits and scones with a
selection of teas, including Assam, Ceylon, China, Darjeeling and Earl Grey.

Closed: all of January and February.

INSTOW

The Commodore Hotel

Marine Parade   Disabled Access

Instow   Parking on site

01271 860347

Set on the seafront and not far from the National Trust Gardens and Tapeley
Park, The Commodore Hotel has superb views from the patio terrace and
the Tea Rooms.

The appetite is satisfied with two scones, Devonshire clotted cream, jam
and a pot of tea. All cakes and scones are home baked and there is a variety
of teas, including Assam, Ceylon, China, Darjeeling and Earl Grey.

Fuchsia Tea Gardens

Fuchsia Valley   Disabled Access
Lee   Parking 100m.
Nr. Ilfracombe
01271 863551

Located opposite "Old Maid's Cottage" in the village centre, the Fuchsia Tea
Garden is close to Sandy Beach and many lovely walks.
There is a small bridge over a stream leading to the tea room and the tea
garden is fronted by a fuchsia hedge. Devon Cream Tea is served, along
with a variety of home baked cakes. In addition to Ceylon and Earl Grey
teas, there is a choice of herb infusions.

LITTLE HAM

Tythe Cottage Tea Rooms

West Down Lane   Disabled Access
Little Ham   Parking on site
Nr. Exmouth
01395 271627

Situated down the road from the church and post office in the village of
Little Ham, Tythe Cottage Tea Rooms are local to Sandy Bay Holiday Park
and the country life museum.
The setting is a fifteenth century listed thatched cottage with a large open
fireplace, beams and olde worlde charm. The decor is typical of the English
tea room.
Stuart and Marion Donohue are the proprietors and offer Devon Cream
Teas, Tythe Barn Teas and a Cheese Tea. Cakes and scones are all home
baked and the teas include Assam, China, Darjeeling and Earl Grey.

LUSTLEIGH   **Devon**

Primrose Cottage Tea Rooms
Lustleigh   Disabled Access
Nr. Newton Abbott   Parking on site
0164 77365

Set opposite the old church in the village of Lustleigh within Dartmoor National Park and with lovely walks and bridle paths close by, Primrose Cottage Tea Rooms has a thatched roof and pretty gardens overlooking the river. Inside, the decor is cosy with charming crockery and a tempting display of cakes in the cabinet.

Cream Tea offers the guest a pot of tea or coffee, two large scones (plain, fruit or wholemeal), clotted cream and two jams. There is also a cheese tea, comprising two scones with Stilton or cheddar and a selection of fresh fruit. Of the many specialities, home made cakes, fresh fruit pavlovas, banoffee pie and chocolate fudge are very popular.

Closed: School half term holidays in February and October.

LYNMOUTH

Priors Cottage
10 Lynmouth Street   Disabled Access
Lynmouth   Parking 100m.
01598 752390

Priors Cottage is situated close to the harbour with local attractions being Exmoor National Park, the water operated cliff railway and the valley of rocks. There are three tea rooms, smoking and non-smoking, each with their own theme. The crockery is willow pattern and one room overlooks the river. There is some outside seating for warm days.

The cream tea is very reasonably priced, serving each guest with a pot of tea, two home made scones, jam and clotted cream. Cakes are also home baked and the teas in the pot include Earl Grey and Lemon.

Closed: Weekdays between mid November and mid March.

Strand Tea Rooms

24 New Street   Disabled Access
Barbican   Parking 50m.
Plymouth
01752 564669

The Strand Tea Rooms are set on the harbourside of the Barbican, close to
Plymouth Hoe and the fishing port.
The Elizabethan building has appropriately period decor inside, where there
are "Tudor" tables and a flagged floor, beamed ceilings and large windows,
with views over the fishing boats moored in the harbour.
Devon Cream Tea uses clotted cream produced on a nearby farm or a
combination of teacake or crumpets plus tea. There is a good selection of teas
including Assam, Ceylon, China, Darjeeling and Earl Grey. Cakes and scones
are home made.

PRINCETOWN

Duchy House Tea Rooms

Duchy House   Parking on site
Tavistock Road
Princetown
01822 890552

Situated in the middle of Dartmoor National Park, Princetown is the highest
town in England. Duchy House can be found opposite Princetown County
Primary School, and commands an outstanding view of Dartmoor from the
town.
The small, family-run business offers a friendly home environment and a
non-smoking zone.
Devon Cream Teas with home made scones and cakes are available, and
there are even home made sweets on sale. The main tea on offer is Earl
Grey.

Closed: Mondays during winter season.

The Parlour Tea Room

112 East Street   Disabled Access
South Molton   Parking 50m.
01769 574144

The Parlour Tea Room is situated next to the garage and close to Quince Honey Farm. Furnished with a 1900s front parlour, gate-leg tables and wheelback chairs, it has an area which sells small antiques.

Devonshire Cream Tea is set alongside a wide range of home made cakes and biscuits cooked on the premises. There are several unusual cakes which change from time to time as the menu is constantly updated. Tea is loose leaf and there are nine different types, including Assam, Darjeeling, Earl Grey, Keemum, Lapsang Souchong, Rose Hip and Camomile. There is also a good selection of soft drinks and other hot beverages.

Closed: Sundays in summer season, Sundays and Mondays during winter season.

TIVERTON

Canal Tea Gardens

Lime Kiln Cottage   Disabled Access
Canal Hill   Parking on site
Tiverton
01884 252291

Not far from the castle and historic market town of Tiverton, the Canal Tea Gardens and covered verandah are set in the grounds of a seventeenth century cottage (Grade II Listed), alongside the canal in a Country Park. The gardens have a fish pond, waterfall, a genuine hollow elm tree and large oak "pixie" tables and chairs.

Cottage Tea serves a sandwich and cake of the customer's choice, a pot of tea or coffee and a scone with clotted cream and jam. Devon Cream Tea offers two scones, a choice of jams, clotted cream and a pot of tea or coffee. Cakes, scones and jams are home made, and teas include Assam, Ceylon, China, Darjeeling and Earl Grey.

Closed: October to March.

Four and Twenty Blackbirds
43 Gold Street   Parking 100m
Lowman Green
Tiverton
01884 257055

At the bottom of Lowman Green Clock Tower, these tea rooms are set below
kerb level in an area known as The Pound. Old beams and a motley assortment of furniture and objets d'art enhance the traditional atmosphere. Fresh
flowers decorate the rooms and an old range with a gas coal fire warms the
main seating area. Antiques are for sale upstairs and there is a warm, friendly
atmosphere throughout.
A wide range of goodies on the menu include home baked scones, cakes and
jams and among the teas are Ceylon, Darjeeling, Earl Grey, Lapsang and
various herb teas.

Closed: Sundays.

TOPSHAM

Georgian Tea Rooms
Broadway House   Disabled Access
35 High Street   Parking 100m.
Topsham
01392 873465

The Georgian Tea Rooms are set in a lovely old town where many of the
houses are of Dutch origin. Nearby is ideal birdwatching country. Built in
1777, the house has a very fine staircase and the hall contains 16th and 17th
century leather panels. In the summer guests can enjoy their tea in a walled,
secluded garden. The tables are covered with embroidered cloths and fresh
flowers and proprietor Heather Knee has won the Heartbeat Award for the
5th year and the tea rooms appear in two Egon Ronay guides. Cakes, scones
and jams are home made and served on pretty bone china. The wide range
of teas includes Assam, Ceylon, China, Rose Pouchong, Lapsang Souchong
and Jasmine.

Closed: Sundays.

TOPSHAM   **Devon**

Tawnys
86 Fore Street   Disabled Access
Topsham   Parking 50m.
01392 877887

Inside Tawny's, the proprietor, Dee Mc Neish, offers a range of local craft items and paintings. The atmosphere is very friendly and homely, epitomising the English tea room.

Afternoon Tea with a slice of home made cake, or the Devon Cream Tea with two home baked scones, Devon clotted cream and jam are reasonably priced and bread comes from the local baker.

There is a good selection of teas, including Assam, Ceylon, China, Darjeeling and Earl Grey and these are supplemented with London Herb and Spice Company Teas.

Closed: Sundays

TORQUAY

Riviera Tea Rooms
4 Braddons Hill Road West   Disabled Access
Torquay   Parking100m.
01803 215399

Next door to the main post office and well-positioned in the centre of town with access to all the shops, the Riviera Tea Rooms are close to the harbourside and sea front.

Inside, the tea is served in large china cups. Proprietor Allen Hindley aims to give his guests excellent value for money with his friendly staff and a warm atmosphere.

The Traditional Devon Cream Tea comes with two home made scones, strawberry jam, clotted cream and a pot of tea or coffee. There is also a wide selection of home baked cakes, banoffee pie, lemon meringue, treacle tart and various gateaux. Earl Grey is the speciality tea.

Closed: Sundays, and October to mid-March.

The Tudor Rose
13-14 Victoria Parade   Parking 100m.
Torquay
01803 296558

Overlooking the harbour and marina, The Tudor Rose is an historic building close to Cockington, the model village and Kent's Cavern.
The interior of the tea rooms was featured in an article in The Times in 1993, and is Tudor, with oakwood panels and dark furniture made in solid oak.
Cream Teas are served with scones and a variety of cakes, all home made. Also available is a wide range of ice cream specialities and the teas include Assam, Ceylon, China, Darjeeling and Earl Grey.

TOTNES

Greys Dining Room
96 High Street   Disabled Access
Totnes   Parking 100m.
01803 866369

Close to the Norman Castle, Greys Dining Room has a Georgian facade with two display windows, each housing a magnificent fern in an urn. One wall of the shop has original wood panels, discovered by the present owners under another wall. The cake display cabinet is Flemish in origin and there are collections of copper, blue and white china and saucers. Tea is served in silver-plated teapots and the entrance to the kitchen is behind a Victorian decoupaged screen.
Cream Tea offers home made scones, two types of jam, clotted cream and a pot of tea. Totnes Tea serves two hot toasted crumpets, a dish of cheddar cheese and a pot of tea or cup of coffee. All cakes are home baked and there is a choice of thirty-seven different teas and infusions.

Closed: Wednesdays.

The Long House

The Square   Disabled Access
West Down   Parking on site
01271 863242

The bright and airy tea room started life as the village smithy in about 1720. For most of this century, the building housed the village shop and post office and, since 1989, the tea room. Exposed stone walls and a mahogany sideboard, which groans daily under the weight of plates of cakes make this a splendid place to take tea.

Traditional Devonshire Cream Tea serves a pot of Long House Blend tea, two scones, jam and local farm clotted cream. Off the Beaten Track tempts guests with a pot of tea, buttered toasted tea cake, meringue, fresh fruit and local clotted cream. All cakes, scones and jams are home made and teas include Assam, Ceylon, China, Darjeeling and Earl Grey.

Closed: Early November until Easter.

-------0-------

*(Tar water) is of a nature so mild and benign
and proportioned to the human constitution as
to warm without heating, to cheer but not inebriate.*

(Bishop George Berkeley, 1744)

ABBOTSBURY   Dorset

The Old Schoolhouse Tea Rooms

1 Back Street   Disabled Access
Abbotsbury   Parking 50m.
01305 871808

The Old Schoolhouse Tea Rooms are in the centre of the village, famous for its swannery. The decor is of the 1930s and 40s, with rose and lace tablecloths, music from that era, walls crammed with old pictures, newspapers and magazine advertisements and waitresses dressed in "Nippy" style black with long white aprons.

Clotted Cream Tea for one is two plain scones with clotted cream and strawberry jam, along with a pot of tea. For those who like to share, in addition, a round of sandwiches of the customer's choice and two pieces of home made fruit cake. Cakes are home baked - including the Dorset apple cake - and among the teas are Assam, Ceylon, Darjeeling and Earl Grey.

Closed: Mondays, Tuesdays and Wednesdays in winter and summer , Tuesdays in summer. Closed during January and first half of February. Closed weekdays in November and December..

BRIDPORT

The Cottage Loaf

25 The Old Shipyard Centre   Parking 50m.
West Bay
Bridport
01308 456991

Situated in a small shopping arcade opposite West Beach, The Cottage Loaf is close to beaches, the River Britt and the fishing harbour.

Proprietors Cyril and Joyce Walford welcome you to a pretty tea room with tables and chairs outside on the patio and a friendly service.

Cream Tea provides hungry visitors with two scones, a pot of jam and one of clotted cream, accompanied by a pot of tea. Cakes and scones are home baked, and specialities to look out for are the deep apple pie and the apple cake. The main tea on offer is Miles Blend.

Closed: Mondays (except Bank Holidays). January and December.

CERNE ABBAS   **Dorset**

The Old Market House
Cerne Abbas   Disabled Access
01300 341680   Parking 50m.

Next to the Royal Oak public house and the Church, The Old Market House is close to the landmark of the Cerne Abbas Giant chalk carving on the hill. The tea room is a Georgian building in the centre of the historic village. It has been used not only as the village market (hence the name), but also as a clockmaker's shop.

Market House Tea comprises two scones, butter, strawberry jam and tea, full Dorset Cream Tea adding a portion of clotted cream. Bread, scones and cakes are all home made and there is a good selection of teas, among them Assam, Ceylon, China, Darjeeling and Earl Grey.

Closed: Tuesdays, and weekdays between November and February.

The Singing Kettle
7 Long Street   Parking 50m.
Cerne Abbas
01300 341349

Established around 1960, The Singing Kettle can be found in the centre of the village opposite the New Inn.

Set in a Georgian building which dates from about 1750, the tea room is furnished with gateleg and antique round tables, Laura Ashley decor and waitress service at all times.

Tea fills the empty guest with two home made scones, jam and clotted cream, along with a pot of tea. Cakes are home baked, and hot Dorset apple cake, treacle tart and large home made meringues with clotted cream are firm favourites with visiting appetites. There is also a very rich fruit cake which is washed down nicely by the Earl Grey tea that is served.

Closed: Mondays, and from November 1st to mid-March.

CHARMOUTH   Dorset

Stow House Tea Room and Garden

The Street   Disabled Access
Charmouth   Parking 50m.
01297 560603

With attentive, friendly service to make each visit a pleasure, owners Derrick and Maureen Kent invite their guests to enjoy the peace and quiet of the charming tea room and historic walled garden. Guests are asked to respect the No Smoking policy.

Cream Tea consists of two home made scones, jam, clotted cream and a pot of tea, or a freshly cut sandwich with a portion of home baked cake (or scone with jam and clotted cream) and pot of tea. Cakes are home made, the favourites being Stow House's own apple cake, rich dark chocolate cake, banana and ginger and rich fruit cake. A good choice of teas include Ceylon, China, Darjeeling and Earl Grey.

Closed: Wednesdays, and October to just before Easter.

CHRISTCHURCH

Ducking Stool Tea Rooms

Ducking Stool Lane   Disabled Access
Christchurch   Parking 50m.
01202 485779

The tea rooms are named after the recently placed Ducking Stool in Mill Stream. The twentieth century scold can drown herself in tea in a civilised atmosphere.

Cream Tea consists of two scones, clotted cream, a choice of jam and tea or coffee. Cheese Tea is the same price for two cheese scones filled with soft cream cheese and a choice of tomato or cucumber relish. Cakes, scones and jam are all home made, the jams are strawberry, blackcurrant or apricot, and the house speciality is "Thunder and Lightning" (bread, cream and syrup). Teas include Assam, Ceylon, Darjeeling and Earl Grey.

Closed: Sundays.

CHRISTCHURCH   **Dorset**

Old Mill Tea Rooms
The Quay   Disabled Access
Quay Road   Parking 50m.
Christchurch
01202 474942

Old Mill Tea Rooms are ideally set in the priory town which is popular wth
visitors who enjoy pretty surroundings. The proprietors are pleased to offer
a good views from their historic building, attractive decor and china.
Cream Tea comprises a pot of tea, two home made scones, a choice of jams
and clotted cream. There are also home made donuts and various ice cream
specials. Earl Grey is the main tea on offer.

Closed: Tuesdays, Wednesdays, Thursdays and Fridays from 1st December
to 23rd February.

DORCHESTER

The Old Tea House
44 High Street   Disabled Access
Dorchester   Parking 50m.
01305 263719

Built in 1635, The Old Tea House can be found at the top end of the town,
close to the museums and the Roman remains.
Inside is an inglenook fireplace and old beams to give an historic ambience.
Cream teas are served with a variety of home baked bread, scones and
cakes. There is a choice of tea, including China and Earl Grey, or coffee for
those who prefer it.

Closed: Mondays, and during the Winter.

DORCHESTER   **Dorset**

Potter In
19 Durngate Street   Disabled Access
Dorchester   Parking 50m.
01305 260312

With a garden entrance to Waitrose and close to the Thomas Hardy and Dinosaur Museums, Potter In is ideally placed for tourists and regulars alike. Its walled garden and patio are a short distance away from the historic part of town and the modern shopping area.

There is a choice of wholemeal, fruit or white scones to be eaten with Dorset clotted cream. In addition to these dainties, rich chocolate or coffee cake, carrot cake and cinnamon toast are supreme favourites with the customers. Bread, scones, cakes and jams are all home made and the selection of teas include Assam, Ceylon, Darjeeling and Earl Grey.

Closed: Sundays (except during June, July and August).

MILTON ABBAS

The Tea Clipper
53A The Street   Parking on site
Milton Abbas
01258 880223

Set in the main street of picturesque village, Milton Abbas, The Tea Clipper is surrounded by thatched, whitewashed cottages. Milton Abbey, Park Farm Museum and the Rare Breeds Centre are local attractions to the Grade Two listed building.

Inside, Dorset cream tea revives the weary traveller with a pot of tea, two warm scones, clotted cream and strawberry jam. Bread, cakes and scones are all home baked on the premises and specialities include Dorset apple cake, and treacle and Bakewell tarts. There is a wide range of teas, featuring Assam, Ceylon, China, Darjeeling and Earl Grey.

Closed: Mondays (except Bank Holidays), weekdays between November and February.

POOLE   **Dorset**

Harts Teashop
112 High Street   Disabled Access
Poole   Parking 50m.
01202 685419

Halfway along the High street opposite Peacocks and Salisbury's, Harts Teashop attracts "shoppers" from the Dolphin Centre and "tourists" from the picturesque Poole Quay with its fishing boats. The shop dates from the 1920s and the proprietors have tried to reflect this in the decor, with bentwood furniture. Pottery is provided by Purbeck Pottery, a local firm, situated on the quay. The atmosphere is warm and friendly.

Tea comprises two fruit scones, butter, clotted (subject to availability during the winter months) or fresh cream, strawberry jam and a pot of tea for one. Cakes are home made and the range of teas include old favourites Assam, Ceylon, Darjeeling and Earl Grey.

SHILLINGSTONE

The Willows
5 Blandford Road   Parking on site
Shillingstone
Nr. Blandford Forum
01258 861167

Set on the eastern side of the village, there is lovely walking and cycling to be enjoyed near to The Willows on Wessex Ridgeway. The building itself is an eighteenth century cob and brick cottage with inglenook fireplace.

The Dorset Cream Tea supplies two scones with jam, butter, clotted cream and a pot of tea. Farmhouse tea consists of a boiled egg with brown bread, a cake from the display cabinet and a pot of tea. Cakes and scones are home made and one favourite out of the variety on offer is the Dorset apple cake, which is served with clotted cream. Teas on offer include Ceylon, Darjeeling and Earl Grey.

Closed: Between November and March.

SWANAGE   **Dorset**

The Old Stable Tea Room
37 Commercial Road   Disabled Access
Off Station Road   Parking 100m.
Swanage
01929 424544

Situated in a seaside town with picturesque surroundings, The Old Stable
is over one hundred years old.
Lace tablecloths, an old fashioned atmosphere and personal service by the
owners, Edward and Joan Noades, make this an ideal place to take tea.
Cream Tea arrives with clotted cream and choice of jam, scones and cakes
are home baked. A good selection includes toasted teacake, Dorset apple
cake and carrot cake, and to wash them down there is a choice of teas
including Assam, Darjeeling and Earl Grey.

Closed: Sundays during winter season (December to March).

WEYMOUTH

Dot's Pantry
40 The Esplanade   Disabled Access
Weymouth   Parking 50m.
01305 786831

Situated on the sea front, opposite the main beach and close to children's
swingboats, helter skelter and donkey rides, Dot's Pantry is a Class Two
listed building.
Inside, the tablecloths and china crockery contribute towards the feel of the
typical tea room.
Dorset Cream Tea serves a pot of tea, a home made scone, strawberry jam
and Dorset clotted cream. Also on the menu are soft ice cream desserts.
Assam is among the teas available.

Closed: End of October to Easter.

WORTH MATRAVERS

Dorset

Worth Tea Shop

Inner Cottage   Disabled Access
Worth Matravers   Parking 100m.
Nr. Swanage
01929 439368

Opposite the village green and duckpond and next to the village shop, Worth Tea Shop boasts an attractive tea garden. It is close to various beautiful coastal walks.

Cream teas are served with home baked scones and cakes. The teas on offer include Assam, Ceylon, China, Darjeeling and Earl Grey.

Closed: Weekdays during winter season (November to March).

-------0-------

Venus her myrtle, Phoebus has his bays;
Tea both excels, which she vouchsafes to praise...
The Muses' friend, tea doth our fancy aid,
Repress those vigours which the head invade,
And keeps that palace of the soul serene.

(Edmund Waller)

BARNARD CASTLE

Durham

The Market Place Teashop

29 Market Place
Barnard Castle
01833 690110

Disabled Access
Parking outside

Situated in the Market Place and near to The Castle, English Heritage and Egglestone Abbey, The Market Place Teashop serves a variety of goodies. All the food is made on the premises and over the years proprietor Robert Hilton has gained a reputation for good food and service.

Closed: Sunday mornings, the Christmas period and Sundays between Christmas and Mother's Day.

-------0-------

Salsify (Mock Oyster) Sandwiches

Put the roots of 3 salsify into cold water, with a wine glass of vinegar and salt. Leave for an hour, then boil until tender and mash with a pint of cream. Add 2 teaspoons of anchovy sauce and cayenne pepper to taste.

(Five O' Clock Tea, 1886)

BLAKE END   Essex

Cottage Craft and Tea Room

Blake House Craft Centre   Disabled Access
Blake End   Parking on site
Nr. Braintree
01376 320662

Within easy access of the A. Clarke Steam Museum and the Braintree Silk
Museum, the Cottage Craft and Tea Room is set in the middle of the craft
centre.
Originally an old cart lodge, the building is Grade Two Listed and sells local
craft items, limited editions and other collectables.
Cream Teas are very reasonably priced and cakes are home made.

BRIGHTLINGSEA

The White Rose Tea Shop

Tower Street   Disabled Access
Brightlingsea   Parking 50m.
01206 305805

In a quiet location just off the High Street and on the road to the harbour,
The White Rose Tea Shop is well-placed in a small coastal town and boating centre. It is within easy walking distance of the promenade, which has
spectacular views over the River Colne.
Tea consists of a scone with butter, jam, fresh cream and a pot of tea. Cakes
are supplied by the local baker and ice cream is also available.

BURNHAM-ON-CROUCH   Essex

The Crooked Cottage Tea Rooms
1 The Quay   Parking 50m.
Burnham-on-Crouch
Essex
01621 783868

Close to the yacht harbour and riverside walks, the tea rooms are housed in 350 year old fishermen's cottages on the quayside. Original timber beams and brick fireplaces give an olde worlde ambience inside, while in warm weather guests can sit in the Victorian rose garden.

Cream Tea serves a pot of tea or coffee, Tiptree jam, fresh cream and two home made scones. Cakes are also home baked and the establishment offers a choice of eighteen types of tea, including favourites Assam, Ceylon, China, Darjeeling and Earl Grey.

Closed: Mondays (except Bank Holidays) and weekdays from November to March).

COLCHESTER

Jacklins Restaurant
147 High Street
Colchester
01206 572157

Established in 1920 on the site of the pottery shop of Roman Colchester, Jacklins is a restaurant and specialist shop for confectionery, teas, coffees and tourist gifts, not far from Colchester Castle Museum, the Clock Museum and the Roman wall and gateway.

Situated on the first floor of the building, the oak-panelled restaurant serves Essex Tea, with buttered teacake, jam, home made cake and a pot of tea of the customer's choice. Special Cream Tea replenishes the empty stomach with home made scones, butter, Tiptree jam and whipped dairy cream as well as a choice of tea such as Assam, Ceylon, China, Darjeeling and Earl Grey.

Closed: Sundays and Bank Holidays.

COGGESHALL   Essex

The Clockhouse Teahouse
Stoneham Street   Parking on site
Coggeshall
01376 563242

Situated in the centre of the town, the building is used as a tourist information centre and houses the village clock, which is open to visitors on summer afternoons. Dating back to the 1450s, the building at one time housed the village school for the poor of the village. The clock was made for Queen Victoria's Jubilee "for the better keeping of time" for the apprentices who worked in the wool trade.

Cream Tea consists of a scone with jam and cream and a pot of tea. All pies, cakes and scones are made on the premises, and can be made to order. Bread and jam is also home made and there is a pleasing range of teas, including Assam, Ceylon, Darjeeling and Earl Grey.

DANBURY

Tea on the Green
Eves Corner   Disabled Access
Danbury   Parking 100m.
Nr. Chelmsford
01245 226616

Set on the village green in the heart of Danbury village, Tea on the Green lives up to its name. Inside it is beautifully decorated in pink, with lace tablecloths and fine white china. In summer outside seating adds to the easy atmosphere.

Traditional Cream Tea offers two large sultana scones with jam and whipped double cream along with any speciality tea or other hot beverage. For children, Village Green Tea provides soup or a sandwich, a fizzy drink, squash or milk and half a portion of cake. Luxury dairy ice creams, home made cakes and scones add to the menu, with over twelve varieties of tea, ground coffees and speciality hot chocolates.

Closed: Sundays.

FINCHINGFIELD

Jemima's Tea Rooms

The Green
Finchingfield
Nr. Braintree
Essex

01371 810605

Disabled Access
Parking 50m.

Set in one of the prettiest villages in England, Jemima's Tea Rooms overlooks the Green and pond. The 400 year old building is resplendent with oak beams and a traditional atmosphere, which it shares with its visitors.

Catering for individuals or coach parties, Cream Teas and other variations provide home made scones and cakes for weary travellers and a choice of Darjeeling and Earl Grey in the pot.

Closed: Weekdays November and December, Mondays and Fridays January to March.

HALSTEAD

Tudor House Tearooms

19 High Street
Halstead

01787 474644

Disabled Access
Parking 50m.

This typical English tea room is a listed Tudor building with exposed original beams and attractive floral decor throughout. The work of local artists and dried flower arrangements are displayed for sale. Along with waitress service, there is a mother and baby changing room, a play table for small children, a highchair and children's menu.

Over twenty mouthwatering types of cakes baked on the premises tempt the waistline, as do the genuine Belgian chocolates sold loose by the pound. Teas include Assam, China, Darjeeling and Earl Grey and several herbal teas, as well as a range of fruit juices, and there are nine varieties of flavoured coffees.

Closed: Sundays.

The Cake Table Tea Room
5 Fishmarket Street
Thaxted
01371 831206

Disabled Access
Parking 100m.

The Cake Table Tea Room is on the left of the six hundred year old Guildhall
with the windmill and church providing additional local interest.
It is easy to see why awards of excellence have been made by the Tea Council.
Traditional chintz fabrics, wheelback chairs, a dresser and open fireplace give
a typically tea room feel. Egon Ronay recommended, old beams and attractive,
double-fronted windows add to the atmosphere. During summer, guests are
able to sit out on the patio.
Cream Tea serving a scone with cream, jam, cake and tea fill the empty visitor.
Or there is a sandwich, cake and tea option. Proprietors Robert and Kathleen
Albon guarantee that all cakes and scones are home made on the premises.
Specials include coffee and walnut cake, chocolate cake, butter or caramel
shortbread and fruit cake. Fifty teas are served, including fruit and herbal
infusions.

Closed: Monday mornings, all day Monday during winter season.

-------0-------

*Oh some are fond of Spanish wine and some are fond of French,
And some'll swallow tay and stuff fit only for a wench.*

(John Masefield - Captain Stratton's Fancy)

BOURTON-ON-THE-WATER   Gloucestershire

Bo-Peep Tea Rooms
Riverside   Disabled Access
Bourton-on-the-Water
Cheltenham
01451 822005

Situated on the edge of the river in this major tourist village, the Bo-Peep Tea Rooms are close to the model village, the motor museum and Birdland Perfumery.

The building is reputedly partly seventeenth century, with antique panelling and Cotswold stone walls. It has been the recipient of Tea Council awards for excellence and was one of the Top Ten tea rooms in 1994.

Cream Teas comprise two large home made scones with strawberry jam, Cornish clotted cream and a pot of leaf tea. There is a range of over forty teas.

CHELTENHAM

Thatchers Tea Shop
101 Montpellier Street   Disabled Access
Cheltenham   Parking on site
01242 584150

To the rear of Cheltenham Ladies' College and opposite the entrance to the bus station, local attractions for visitors to Thatchers Tea Shop are the Cotswolds, National Hunt Racing, and the spa town itself.

Tea is served within the prettily decorated tea room. Two scones, thick Cornish clotted cream, strawberry jam and a pot of tea comprise the Cream Tea, or as an alternative, two slices of bread and butter, jam and a choice of cake, with the pot of tea. Scones are home made and there are ice cream specialities and sorbets as well as a good range of teas, including Assam, Ceylon, China, Darjeeling, Earl Grey and Lapsang Souchong.

CHIPPING CAMPDEN   Gloucestershire

Greenstocks at the Cotswold House
The Square   Parking on site
Chipping Campden
01386 840330

Adjacent to the Cotswold House Hotel, the tea rooms are in the medieval town famous for its market hall and historic high street.
The building itself dates from 1650 and is home to many antiques. There is a willow-shaded courtyard in summer.
Cakes and scones are home baked. Proprietors, Mr. and Mrs. Greenstock's toffee meringues and Danish pastries are famous. Among the teas are Assam, Ceylon, Darjeeling and Earl Grey.

MORETON-IN-MARSH

The Marshmallow
High Street   Disabled Access
Moreton-in-Marsh   Parking on site
01608 651536

The Marshmallow is to be found at the Stratford end of Moreton on the High Street. It is close to Batsford Falconry and Arboretum.
The Grade Two Listed building is ivy clad in front, and boasts a spectacular patio with hanging baskets. Inside the decor is peach, white and green. Leather bound books and pottery line the shelves and with exposed beams and cotswold stone provide a feast for the eyes.
Cream Teas provide a more substantial feast, serving a huge scone with all the trimmings. Bread, cakes, scones and jams are all home made and there is a good selection of gorgeous gateaux. Among the teas are Assam, Ceylon, China, Darjeeling and Earl Grey.

Chancellor's Tea Rooms and Restaurant

Kingsley House   Disabled Access
Victoria Street   Parking 50m.
Painswick
Nr. Stroud
01452 812451

Set in the centre of the village near the stocks, The Chancellors Tea Rooms
are within easy reach of Painswick House and gardens. The Grade II listed
building in Cotswold stone with oak beams is a good setting for a traditional
English Tea.
Cream Tea comprises two scones, jam, cream and a pot of tea, and the
Chancellor's Special Afternoon Tea offers egg mayonnaise and cress sandwich,
home made fruit scone with butter and jam and a pot of tea. Scones and cakes
are home made and teacakes can be served with a special cinnamon butter.
Among a good selection of teas are the old favourites Assam, Ceylon, China,
Darjeeling and Earl Grey.

Closed: Wednesdays during winter season.

WINCHCOMBE

Lady Jane's Tea Shop

Thailes Street   Disabled Access
Winchcombe   Parking 100m.
01242 603578

Lady Jane's Tea Shop enjoys views over the hills and fields from the patio.
The building is picturesque, with some Cotswold stone walls and beams, an
inglenook fireplace and well-decorated interior in navy and pink, with fresh
flowers on the tables and china teapots.
The Local's Tea comprises thick, toasted fruit bread and a choice of home
made cake, or the Winter Warmer Tea serves two hot, buttered crumpets with
jam and a choice of home made cake. Clotted Cream Teas are a speciality and
among the teas available are Assam, China, Darjeeling and Earl Grey.

Closed: End of January to mid-March.

The Olde Bakery Tea Shoppe
High Street   Disabled Access
Winchcombe   Parking 50m.
01242 602469

Close to the town square and on the corner of Castle Street, The Olde Bakery
Tea Shoppe is on The Cotswold Way and not far from Sudley Castle and
Toddington Railway. Approximately three hundred years old, the Cotswold
stone building has two tea rooms and a conservatory leading into a walled tea
garden. In the winter cosy fires warm the chilly visitor, along with the Fireside
Tea, which provides a pot of tea and two crumpets with butter, strawberry jam
and cake from the selection on the tray.
The Cotswold Cream Tea includes two scones, strawberry jam and fresh cream
with a pot of tea. Scones and cakes are home made and the tea shop is famous
for its carrot cake. Among the teas on the menu are Assam, Ceylon, China,
Darjeeling and Earl Grey.

Closed: Mondays (except Bank Holidays) and four weeks during January/
February.

--------0---------

THE POETS AT TEA
(MACAULAY)

Pour, varlet, pour the water,
The water steaming hot!
A spoonful for each man of us,
Another for the pot!

Barry Pain
1864-1928

Sea Cottage Tea Shoppe
Marine Drive   Parking 50m.
Barton-on-Sea
01425 614086

On a cliff top overlooking The Needles and Isle of Wight, the tea shop has traditional cottage decor and presents the healthier food options which have won proprietors Kevin and Wendy Noon a Healthy Heartbeat Award for three consecutive years. The nautically themed menu washes up for High Tide two scones, clotted cream and a choice of strawberry, apricot or blackcurrant jam with a pot of tea. Full Sail replaces the windblown guest's lost energy with a pot of tea, assorted finger sandwiches, two scones, clotted cream and a choice of jam. Produce is home made, and there is a wide selection of cakes and pastries. Teas include Assam, Ceylon, China, Darjeeling and Earl Grey.

Closed: Mondays during winter season, and all of January.

BROCKENHURST

The Tea Shoppe
37 Brookley Road   Parking 100m.
Brockenhurst
01590 622120

Near to the ford in Brockenhurst, The Tea Shoppe, with its beamed ceiling and friendly atmosphere, is within walking distance of the New Forest. New Forest Cream Tea provides two home made scones with butter, conserve and Cornish clotted cream, accompanied by a pot of tea. The Hovis Tea comes with Hovis bread or toast and butter and jam with a pot of tea, whilst the Old English Tea fills the grumbling stomach with teacakes and jam with a pot of tea. For those who prefer, there is coffee or a cold drink. As well as the very good Bon Hamman French jam, locally produced honey and fudge are on sale. The teas in the pot include Ceylon, China, Darjeeling and Earl Grey.

Closed: Sundays between November and Easter.

Thatched Cottage Hotel and Restaurant

16 Brookley Road   Disabled Access
Brockenhurst   Parking on site
01590 623090

The Thatched Cottage has log fires in the lounge, lace tablecloths and fresh flowers on every table. It has been invited to become a member of the Tea Council Guild of Tea Shops. Canaries sing in the tea room, which is filled with antiques, rugs and decorative objects from around the world. The Complete Cream Tea lives up to its name, offering three small finger sandwiches: cucumber, ham and cream cheese and tomato, three scones, plain, fruit and brown with walnuts, two cakes and a biscuit. All bread, cakes, scones and jams are home made, and among the teas poured from the collection of china teapots are Assam, Ceylon, China, Darjeeling and Earl Grey.

Closed: Mondays; Mondays to Thursdays in January and February.

BURLEY

Manor Farm Tea Rooms

Ringwood Road   Disabled Access
Burley   Parking on site
01425 402218

Manor Farm Tea Rooms are in an original thatched cottage, established in 1904. Original oak beams, inglenook fireplace and log fire during the winter make this a cosy place to take tea.
Cream Tea consists of two scones, blackcurrant jam and clotted cream with tea or coffee. Hampshire High Tea offers a savoury sandwich, two slices of bread and butter, a scone with blackcurrant jam and clotted cream, cake and tea or coffee. Renowned for the home made scones and the jams that are made to the specifications of the proprietors, Peter and Kathy Hunt, bread and cakes are also home baked, and teas available include Assam, Ceylon, China, Darjeeling and Earl Grey.

Closed: Monday all day during winter season, Monday mornings during summer season.

EMSWORTH   **Hampshire**

Flint Stones Tea Room
The Quay   Parking on site
South Street
Emsworth
01243 377577

The 17th century flint building on the Quay at the end of the Emsworth Channel is part of the picturesque Chichester Harbour. There is a popular area around the millpond adjacent to Langstone Harbour.

The distinctive interior offers a selection of cakes, including cheese cakes, passion cake and fresh cream goodies. Locombe Farm and soft ice cream are available as are various milk shakes, and Cream Tea serves two scones, clotted cream and jam with a pot of tea. Bread, scones and cakes are all home baked and the range of teas features favourites Assam, Ceylon, China, Darjeeling and Earl Grey.

Closed: Weekdays during winter season.

EXBURY

Exbury Catering
Exbury Gardens   Disabled Access
Exbury   Parking on site
01703 898737

The tea rooms are next to the plant centre at Exbury Gardens. The remarkable two hundred acre woodland garden, created by Lionel de Rothschilds, overlooks Beaulieu River. In Spring there are spectacular displays of rhododendrons, azaleas, camellias and magnolias.

There is a choice of menu for afternoon tea, a typical mid-range one comprising tea or coffee with a cream and jam scone, or at the top of the scale, tea or coffee, a sandwich, cake and jam and cream scone. Cakes and scones are home made and specialities include carrot cake, bread pudding, lemon cake and coffee cake. Teas include Assam, Ceylon, China, Darjeeling and Earl Grey.

Closed: From 30th October to 16th February.

Hamble Tea Rooms

High Street   Disabled Access

Hamble   Parking 50m.

Nr. Southampton

01703 455583

Set in Hamble Square and made famous by its appearances in the TV programme Howard's Way, Hamble Tea Rooms are situated five minutes away from the Hamble River Marina, which offers boat trips to where Howard's way was televised.

The tea rooms go back to the late 18th/early 19th century. The building is picturesque with a garden patio seating area.

LYNDHURST

Mad Hatter Tea Rooms

10 High Street   Disabled Access

Lyndhurst   Parking 100m.

01703 282341

Situated opposite the Crown Hotel and below the church that is the burial place of Lewis Carroll's real-life Alice, the tea rooms are within walking distance of the New Forest.

There is a roof garden where tea can be enjoyed in fine weather, but the Mad Hatter Cream Tea can be enjoyed all year round. Cream Tea's two scones with jam and clotted cream make a party for tired guests. Scones are home made plain, fruit and date and walnut. Cakes are also home baked and various gateaux are available. The teapot is definitely not home to the dormouse in this establishment, but visitors can enjoy teas such as Assam, Darjeeling and Earl Grey.

Closed: November or January.

ROMSEY   Hampshire

Cobweb Tea Rooms
49 The Hundred   Parking to rear
Romsey
01794 516434

Cobweb Tea Rooms, within easy access of Romsey Abbey, is a Georgian property with hanging baskets, oak beams and a delightful enclosed patio garden in the summer. Waitress service and a No Smoking policy make a pleasant atmosphere. A toy box makes children welcome. Cream Teas consist of two scones, with jam, cream and tea. Winter Tea presents two boiled eggs, brown and white bread and butter and tea. Cakes and scones are home baked with a wide variety to choose from. Child sized portions and feeding cups can be provided. As well as various herbal teas, there is Assam, Ceylon, China, Darjeeling and Earl Grey.

Closed: Sundays and Mondays.

SHERFIELD-ON-LODDON

Hartley's Tea Room
MJS Garden Centre   Disabled Access
Wildmoor Lane   Parking on site
Sherfield-on-Loddon
Nr. Basingstoke
01256 800529

Hartley's Tea Room is set in the garden centre. Inside Victorian-style decor with Laura Ashley fabrics and an oak dresser create a traditional feel. Tea is served by waitresses in Liberty print dresses and lace aprons. Summer seating is available beneath the plant-hung pergola.
Hartley's Set Afternoon Tea provides a selection of finger sandwiches, scones with clotted cream and preserve, toasted teacake, a selection of Hartley's home made cakes and a pot of tea. Chineham Tea comes without the sandwiches, whilst the Sherfield tea comprises scones, cream and preserves. The teas include Assam, Ceylon, China, Darjeeling and Earl Grey.

Wickham Teahouse
Wickham   Parking in square
01329 835017

Wickham Teahouse is set in the Square of the pretty Meon Valley village,
with walks in nearby Bere Forest.
The building itself has old beams that are old ships' timber and an open fire,
with views of the old market square from the windows. Most of the shops
are family run businesses.
Cream Tea offers a pot of tea, a buttered scone, jam and clotted cream.
Cakes are home baked and the teapots are full of teas such as Ceylon and
Earl Grey.

-------0-------

THE POETS AT TEA
(TENNYSON)

I think that I am drawing to an end:
For on a sudden came a gasp for breath,
And stretching of the hands, and blinded eyes,
And a great darkness falling on my soul.
O Hallelujah!...Kindly pass the milk.

Barry Pain
1864-1928

Merchants Tea Rooms
78-80 Load Street   Parking 100m.
Bewdley
01299 402436

Situated on the riverside and near to the safari park and Wyre Forest, Merchants Tea Rooms is housed in an historic building and enjoys attractive decor.
Merchants Afternoon Tea and Cream Tea serve a selection of home made cakes and scones. Jams are also home made and Earl Grey is the favourite speciality tea.

BROADWAY

Tisanes
The Green   Parking 100m.
Broadway
01386 852112

Close to the Cotswolds and to be found behind the War Memorial on the village green, Tisanes is an intimate English tea room with a continental touch and quick, efficient waitress service.
There is no set tea menu as all items are individually priced. Hot filled sandwiches at tea time, such as turkey, brie and garlic, bacon brie and avocado or chicken, ham and cheese must be favourites and there is an assortment of sweet specialities such as carrot cake, Dutch apple flan and chocolate fudge cake.
Loose leaf tea includes Assam, Ceylon, China, Darjeeling and Earl Grey or special hot drinks offer hot chocolate with cream and cognac, spiced tea or choco express.

Closed: Thursdays; and all of January and February.

Janes, The Antique Teashop

5A St. Peter's Street   Disabled Access
Hereford   Parking100m.
01432 342172

The building is early Georgian and is on the site of St. Peter's monastery. Tables with linen cloths and fresh flowers do not seem unusual in a tea room. What is different is that the guests sit on and at furniture that is for sale. Pictures on the walls and mirrors are also for sale, making this is a highly individual place to stop for refreshment.

Traditional Cream Tea served on bone china is a scone with clotted cream, strawberry jam and a pot of tea. Traditional Afternoon Tea provides the above, together with a selection of finger sandwiches and cakes or pastries. Bread, scones, cakes and jams are all home made and the Twinings speciality teas are Assam, Ceylon, China, Darjeeling, Earl Grey, Gunpowder, Rose Pouchong and Oolang Keemun.

-------0-------

*Love and scandal are the
best sweetness of tea*

(Henry Fielding)

Kenchester Tea Rooms

Church Road   Disabled Access
Lyde   Parking on site
Nr. Hereford
01432 270891

Situated in the grounds of Kenchester Water Gardens, one of the largest aquatic centres in the country, Kenchester Tea Rooms boasts local sights of water lily displays, tropical, marine and cold water fish and extensive aquatic planting.
During the summer, tea can be taken onto the terrace outside overlooking the lake. Cream Tea comprises a scone with jam and cream and a pot of tea, or with sandwiches and cake. Cakes and scones are home made, and the speciality tea is usually Earl Grey.

MALVERN

Lady Foley's Tea Room

Great Malvern Station   Disabled Access
Imperial Road   Parking on site
Malvern
01684 893033

Set on the platform of a very attractive Victorian railway station which has won awards and been used for television plays, Lady Foley's Tea Room offers tables on the platform for train lovers to watch the trains, whilst inside the decor is in keeping with the building.
Tea supplies the guest with a sandwich, a slice of cake, a scone with jam and cream and a pot of tea. Cakes and scones are all home baked and include goodies like cherry and pineapple cake, date apple and walnut and lemon meringue pie. Teas include Assam, China, Darjeeling and Earl Grey.

The Kettle Sings
Jubilee Drive   Parking on site
Upper Colwall
01684 540244

Situated on the upper western slopes of the Malvern Hills, overlooking rural Herefordshire and beyond, The Kettle Sings has fantastic views from its conservatory. Traditional decor with pink and lace tablecloths, pictures by local artists for sale on the walls and postcards and greeting cards for sale make this a typical English tea room.
Waitress service brings a home made scone with butter, jam and cream or there is a variety of other delicacies, including delicious home made ice cream and toasted teacakes. Cakes and jams are home made, and still or sparkling Malvern water is available as well as Assam, Darjeeling or Earl Grey teas.

Closed: Tuesdays during January and February.

WITHINGTON

Cross Keys Tea Room
The Old Office   Disabled Access
Withington   Parking on site
Nr. Hereford
01432 820600

The Cross Keys Tea Room is two hundred yards from the Cross Keys public house and within easy reach of Hereford Cathedral.
The tea room and grounds are next door to the caravan site for C.L. members only. Cream Teas are served and the speciality tea is Earl Grey.

Closed: Thursdays and Friday mornings, from end of October to end of March.

BERKHAMSTED   Hertfordshire

Castle Tea Room
14 Castle Street   Disabled Access
Berkhamsted   Parking on site
01442 866974

Close to Castle Tea Room is Berkhamsted School and the parish church of St. Peter's, and the ruined castle where William the Conqueror was offered the crown of England. Inside the style is Edwardian, with lace cloths, fresh flowers and natural wood tables, chairs and floors. Newspapers are available daily. Farmhouse Tea offers a pot of tea, sandwich and side salad, a choice of cakes from the sideboard or a buttermilk scone with jam and clotted cream. Fireside Tea serves tea, a boiled egg with buttered toast and the scone, jam and cream. Irish Brack bread, cakes scones and jams are home made and specialities include Bakewell tart and flapjacks. Twenty leaf teas ensure that the contents of the pot are never dull.

Closed: Mondays (except Bank Holidays).

BISHOPS STORTFORD

The Jolly Teapot
Castle House   Parking 50m.
12 Market Square
Bishops Stortford
01279 501307

Found at the rear of The Corn Exchange, The Jolly Teapot enjoys the bustle of the market and the beautiful period buildings in the town. Part of the building dates back to the sixteenth century, with two large inglenook fireplaces which lend a cosy atmosphere to the rooms in winter. In summer, tea may be taken on the patio amongst abundant and colourful flowers, and newspapers and magazines are available.
There is no set menu, but home baked cakes and scones are well-priced, and there is a good range of teas, including Assam, Ceylon, China, Darjeeling and Earl Grey.

Closed: Sundays during winter season.

St. Mary's Tearooms

1 Churchyard   Disabled Access

Hitchin   Parking 100m.

01462 458844

St. Mary's Tearooms enjoy a first class location opposite the historical St. Mary's Church and twenty five metres from the market square.

Inside, the visitor is welcomed in olde worlde style with the oak beams and paintings and sketches by a local artist.

Cream Tea is extremely popular, with two scones, strawberry jam, fresh double cream and a choice of tea or coffee. All food orders are made freshly in the kitchen, and the bread, cakes and scones are bought from Simmons, the local baker. Teas brew in abundance and feature Assam, Ceylon, China, Darjeeling and Earl Grey.

KINGS LANGLEY

The Wishing Well

67 The High Street   Disabled Access

Kings Langley   Parking 50m.

01923 400119

Located to the rear of the Wishing Well Gift Shop, the tea rooms are set in a pretty village with many interesting shops.

The cosy little tea room serves food in pleasant surroundings, where paintings by local artists adorn the walls. Traditional tea room fare is available, with a variety of home made cakes to be enjoyed. Teas include Ceylon, Darjeeling and Earl Grey as well as herb and fruit infusions.

Closed: Sundays, the month of August and Christmas/New Year.

RICKMANSWORTH   **Hertfordshire**

Chenies Manor House

Chenies   Disabled Access
Rickmansworth   Parking on site
01494 762888

Near the parish church in the centre of the village, the tea room is open to visitors to the fifteenth/sixteenth century house and gardens.

Set in the large "orangery" opening to the beautiful gardens, the decor is period and attractive. The moderate prices are by items, with scones and cakes being home made. Coffee is available to those who want it and there is a good range of teas, including Assam, Ceylon, China, Darjeeling and Earl Grey.

Closed: Wednesdays, Thursdays and Bank Holiday Mondays, and from October to March.

ST ALBANS

Abigail's Tearooms

The Village Arcade   Disabled Access
7 The High Street   Parking 100m.
St. Albans
01727 856939

The tearooms are part of a small collection of speciality shops built in the style of St. Albans past. Adjacent to the Clock Tower, they are within easy reach of Verulamium's Roman ruins and St. Alban's Cathedral. In previous times, this was the site of J. Lyons' Tearooms. The current proprietors have preserved the original marble on the arcade walls. Inside, the Tearooms are waitress service, with comfortable tables, lace tablecloths and curtains.

Set Afternoon Tea for One supplies one round of sandwiches, a fruit scone with clotted cream and jam and a piece of cake served with tea. Cakes and scones are home made, all traditional and made to order. Real West Country clotted cream is served with the cakes, and ice creams and sundaes are also available. Among the teas supplied are Assam, Ceylon, Darjeeling and Earl Grey.

Chapter House Refectory

St. Albans Abbey   Disabled Access
Sumpter Yard   Parking 100m.
St. Albans
01727 864208

Adjacent to the Cathedral on the ground floor of the Chapter House, the Refectory is a purpose built room in a modern Chapter House attached to the historic Abbey (founded 793AD, rebuilt 1077AD) and Cathedral Church. The light and airy room has modern, attractive architectural features. The food is freshly made each day, using good ingredients and there is no set menu, allowing customers to choose their favourites. A scone with butter and jam or selection of cakes are well-priced, with Bakewell tart a speciality. Teas available include Assam, Ceylon, Darjeeling and Earl Grey.

Closed: Good Friday, Christmas Bank Holidays.

Gatsby's Tea Room

17 High Street   Parking 100m.
St. Albans
01727 811890

Situated at the rear of a fourteenth century building, with a brick fireplace and exposed timber vaulted roof, Gatsby's is fifty yards from the Abbey and opposite the Clock Tower.
Inside, there are pink and white tablecloths, an Axminster carpet and silk flower fire screen. Family friendly, Gatsby's offer a children's menu and baby-changing facilities.
Afternoon Tea is served, comprising a selection of sandwiches, a scone with clotted cream and jam, a choice of gateaux and a cup of tea. There is an extensive range of home made cakes and various flavoured coffees and teas, including Assam, Ceylon, Darjeeling and Earl Grey.

The Waffle House, Kingsbury Watermill Ltd.

St. Michael's Street
St. Albans   Parking on site
01727 853502

Set by the River Ver in an old Watermill that dates back to Elizabethan times, The Waffle House is half a mile from the Cathedral and close to the Roman remains. The mill itself is now a museum, having been in use until 1936 and then being restored in 1973.

In season there is ample seating outside, next to the picturesque stream. Inside there is also a small shop selling pottery and gifts.

The speciality is freshly baked to order, light and crispy Belgian style wholewheat or plain waffles. The most popular for afternoon tea is Spiced Fruit, where spice covered currants and raisins are baked into the waffle and sprinkled with cinnamon sugar. Pecan and butterscotch, coconut and plain with a variety of toppings such as maple syrup or honey and for a little extra can be enjoyed with ice cream or fresh cream. Along with the old favourites Ceylon, Darjeeling and Earl Grey there are herbal teas, filtered coffees and chilled drinks.

Closed: Mondays.

-------0-------

*Don't pour out tea before putting sugar in the cup,
or some one will be drowned.*

(American Negro Proverb)

The Tea Shop

43A Market Place   Disabled Access
South Cave   Parking on site
01430 423038

Opposite the post office on the main road through the village, The Tea Shop is on the Wolds Way and set in a village that is definitely worth a look around.

The traditional tea shop offers a wide variety of individually priced items on the menu. Cakes, scones and pies are all baked on the premises, one of the most popular specialities being the teabread. All the meat is home cooked as well, so that sandwiches can be a truly healthy option. In fact proprietors Dena Wood and Jane Forsey have just won a Heartbeat Award.

Sandwiches and cakes make a filling and inexpensive tea. The favourite teas available are Assam, Darjeeling and Earl Grey.

Closed: Wednesdays.

------0-------

Tea, A Poem

Tea! How I tremble at thy fatal stream?
As Lethe, dreadful to the Love of Fame.
What devastations on thy banks are seen
What shades of mighty Names which once have been
A hecatomb of Characters supplies
Thy painted Altar's daily sacrifice.

(Aaron Ward)

Marples Tea Rooms
6 Sea View Street   Disabled Access
Cleethorpes   Parking 50m.
South Humberside
01472 697188

Situated in the old part of Cleethorpes, Sea View Street provides a good selection of gift, antique and interior design shops.

Marples is set on the sea front end of the street and is based on the famous Miss Marples theme. Proprietor David Allen prides his establishment on a high level of customer service and high quality products, served in a relaxing and old fashioned environment.

Marples Full Afternoon Tea comprises a freshly cut sandwich, a scone with whipped cream and preserve a choice of sweet from the display and a pot of tea. Marples Traditional Cream Tea provides a scone with cream and jam and a pot of tea. Cakes and scones are freshly made and there is a wide selection of jams and other preserves of all kinds. Freshly ground coffee and teas, including Assam, Ceylon, China, Darjeeling and Earl Grey slake the thirst.

-------0-------

This is the most magnificent movement of all! There is a dignity, a majesty, a sublimity, in this last effort of the patriots that I greatly admire.

The people should never rise without doing something to be remembered - something notable and striking. This destruction of the tea is so bold, so daring, so firm, intrepid and inflexible, and it must have so important consequences, and so lasting, that I cannot but consider it as an epocha in history!

(John Adams' Diary on the day of the Boston Tea Party, 17th Dec, 1773)

Penny Plain Tea Room and Garden

44 High Street   Disabled Access
Brading   Parking 50m.
01983 407649

Situated opposite the old Town Hall with a view of the stocks, Penny Plain
Tea Room is not far from the Isle of Wight Wax Museum and Lilliput Dolls'
Museum.

The quaint tea room atmosphere is enhanced by twenties and thirties dance
music, and in warm weather, guests can sit out in the large patio garden.

Scones and gateaux are home made, with cream teas serving up in season
fresh strawberries and clotted cream. Among other house specials are the
hot scotch pancakes with real maple syrup and double cream, topped with
roast almonds. Tea or coffee is available, the teas including Darjeeling and
Earl Grey.

Closed: Fridays, and from November to February.

GODSHILL

The Old World Tea Gardens

High Street   Disabled Access
Godshill   Parking 50m.
01983 840637

Set opposite the Chapel, The Old World Tea Gardens are local to the ancient
church on the hill, the model village, toy museum and Natural History Centre.
Cream Tea comprises a pot of tea with two scones, jam and a choice of whipped
or clotted cream.

Strawberry tart, strawberry meringue glace, fruit cakes and cream slices are
among the specials, which are all home made. In addition to these, a Diabetic
Cream Tea is a very sensible and healthy option. Earl Grey and Carisbrooke
blend are among the beverages on offer.

Closed: November to mid-March.

GODSHILL

Willow Tree Tea Gardens
High Street
Godshill
01983 840633

Disabled Access
Parking 100m.

Willow Tree Tea Gardens has a sheltered, large garden in the centre of the village. In season, this is a sun trap for customers to enjoy tea. Inside are large separate smoking and non-smoking dining rooms.

Cream Tea consists of two large home made scones, a pot of Baxter's strawberry jam, butter, a large portion of whipped cream and a pot of tea. Bread and cakes are also home baked, with house specials including deep apple pie, bread pudding, cheesecake and strawberry cream tarts made from local strawberries and fresh cream. Earl Grey and Kenya are among the teas on offer.

Closed: November to Easter.

SHANKLIN

Dunnose Cottage Tea Rooms and Gardens
Luccombe Chine
Nr. Shanklin
01983 862585

Disabled Access
Parking on site

Nestling in a secluded valley on National Trust land, Dunnose Cottage is set in three and a half acres of its own award winning gardens. The gardens specialise in herbaceous borders and roses, whilst the building is sixteenth century Grade II listed, decorated inside with traditional wood panelling and feature fireplace. The polished tables and wheelback chairs give an olde worlde feel.

Waitress service brings the variety of goodies on offer. Clotted cream teas with home made scones and home baked cakes such as chocolate fudge, coffee and walnut and carrot vie with the meringues for popularity. Along with the fruit and herbal teas, Darjeeling and Earl Grey are on offer.

Closed: Mondays (except Bank Holidays), weekdays in winter season (November to Easter).

Keats Cottage Tea Rooms

76 High Street
Shanklin Old Village
01983 866351

Disabled Access
Parking 100m.

The old village has much for sightseers, including Shanklin Chine, Sandown Bay's sandy beach and various walks.

Keats Cottage is unique, combining one of Shanklin's historic old buildings with the modern exterior of an up-to-date small hotel. It was formerly "Eglantine Cottage" where the poet John Keats stayed in 1819 to finish Act One of "Otho the Great".

There is no set menu. Customers can make their own selections from the individual items available. Clotted cream teas supply two scones with butter, jam and fresh clotted cream and either a pot of tea or cup of coffee. Scones and cakes are home made, and freshly made sandwiches offer a variety of fillings as do the traditional Yorkshire puddings. Among the teas available are Assam, Darjeeling and Earl Grey.

Closed: Sundays, October to Easter.

Luccombe Tea Gardens

Luccombe Cliff
Nr. Shanklin
01983 863116

Parking on site

Set on a beautiful coastal walk, Luccombe Tea Gardens enjoy a spectacular location where peace and clean air reign. Seating is mainly outside, being very much a tea garden. This venue is generally more suited to walkers than car drivers.

Cream Tea offers the hungry walker two home made scones with jam, clotted cream and a pot of tea. Cakes are also home made, and teas to wash it all down include Ceylon and Earl Grey.

The Old Thatch Tea Shop

4 Church Road
Shanklin
01983 863184

Disabled Access
Parking 100m.

Situated in the centre of the old village, close to the Crab Inn and Chine entrance, The Old Thatch is believed to be three hundred years old. In 1846 it became Shanklin's first Post Office and also had a circulating library and bookshop. It was converted to a tea shop in the 1940s.

The Old Thatch Cream Tea comprises home made scones cooked in the Aga, strawberry preserve and delicious clotted farmhouse cream with a pot of tea. Cakes, too, are home baked, and there is a choice of teas, including Ceylon, Darjeeling and Earl Grey.

Closed: End November to beginning of March.

Vernon Cottage Tea Rooms

1 Eastcliff Road
Shanklin
01983 863588

Disabled Access
Parking 50m.

Set in the old village conservation area and close to the seaside resort of Shanklin Chine, Vernon Cottage is a pretty thatched cottage with a large garden, historically linked to Admiral Lord Vernon. A tunnel used to lead from the site to the chine in the days when smuggling was rife. Although now filled in, there is an air of the old times about the Tea Rooms, furthered by the beautifully carved wooden fireplaces, dating from the 1690s and presumably part of the original cottage.

Proprietors John and Mandy Tiedeman serve Cream Tea which stops hunger pangs with two scones with butter, jam and clotted cream and a pot of tea. The very hungry may want to add a slice of one of the home made cakes. High quality teas include Assam and Earl Grey. Coffee is also available.

Closed: End October to Easter.

BIDDENDEN

Claris's
1-3 High Street
Biddenden
Nr. Ashford
01580 291025

Disabled Access
Parking 50m.

Part of a row of Grade I listed buildings on the village green, Claris's is near to the vineyards and the home of the famous Siamese twins. The building was originally built to house weavers for the wool trade. Oak beams and two inglenook fireplaces remain and there is a small garden. Inside, white china on lace tablecloths enhances the rooms, which are Non-Smoking throughout. A gift shop shares the site.

Cream Tea furnishes the customer with a pot of tea, two scones, butter, a choice of five Baxter's jams and local cream. Choice is varied, with items made from the best of ingredients. Teas include Assam, Ceylon, Darjeeling and Earl Grey.

Closed: Mondays, and 2 weeks after New Year.

BOROUGH GREEN

The Tea House
17 High Street
Borough Green
Nr. Sevenoaks
01732 883073

Disabled Access
Parking 50m.

The Tea House building dates from the 18th century, with Victorian additions when it became a butchers shop for a while. Wooden beams and open fires in winter create a traditional atmosphere in which to take Afternoon Special. This provides a pot of tea with a scone, jam and cream, a choice of sandwiches and home made cake. Cakes, scones and jams are home made, house favourites being chocolate fudge, meringues and cream cakes. Among the teas are Assam, Darjeeling and Earl Grey. Highchairs are available for children, and there are designated Smoking and Non-Smoking areas.

Closed: Sundays and Mondays; for 3 weeks after Christmas, and first week in October.

CHIDDINGSTONE   **Kent**

The Village Tea Shop
3 The Village   Disabled Access
Chiddingstone   Parking 50m.
Nr. Edenbridge
01892 870326

The Village Tea Shop is part of the Burghersh Court, owned at one time by the family of Ann Boleyn, hapless second wife of Henry VIII.
Plain Scone Tea consists of a pot of tea with two scones, butter and jam. Local Cream Scone Tea adds cream. Cakes and scones are home baked and the selection is wide, including various gateaux , cheesecakes and chocolate fudge cake. Teas include Assam, Ceylon, China, Darjeeling and Earl Grey, or there are filter coffees, soft drinks and mineral waters for those who prefer them.
The Village Tea Shop is a member of Les Routiers and the Guild of Tea Shops.

Closed: Mondays, and from December to end of February.

FOLKESTONE

Charlotte Emily Victorian Tea Rooms
4 The Old High Street   Disabled Access
Folkestone   Parking 50m.
01303 220732

The Tea Rooms are close to the beautiful "Old Bayle" and the harbour.
As the name hints, the tea rooms have a Victorian theme, with waitresses dressed in Victorian style as they serve such delicacies as Cream Tea, which provides egg and cucumber sandwich, a scone, jam and cream with a cake of the customer's choice and a pot of tea or coffee.
Cakes are home made, with a delightful carrot cake and bread and butter pudding tempting the palate. There is a good selection of teas including Assam, Ceylon, China, Darjeeling and Earl Grey.

Elan Arts Centre
Sundridge Road
Ide Hill
Nr. Sevenoaks
01732 750344

Disabled Access
Parking 100m.

Set opposite the green, Elan Arts Centre is well-known as a unique gift shop with the paintings of many local artists on view throughout the shop and tea room. There is no set menu, but lots of choice for visitors. Cakes, scones and jams are home made, and there is a variety of scones: cheese, white, wholewheat fruit and walnut and ginger. Speciality cakes include peach, walnut and carrot and chocolate fudge, all reasonably priced, with a selection of favourite teas: Assam, Ceylon, Darjeeling and Earl Grey.

Closed: Mondays and Tuesdays.

LAMBERHURST

Lamberhurst Tearooms
Lamberhurst Down
Lamberhurst
01892 890891

Disabled Access
Parking on site

Opposite Lamberhurst Vineyard, Lamberhurst Tearooms are close to many National Trust properties. The 18th century property was built as four cottages, and retains the wooden beam, two inglenook fireplaces, and a cosy yet elegant ambience.
The tables are decked with pretty linen tablecloths, tasteful cutlery and bone china throughout. Nora Batty Tea offers pot of tea or cafetiere of coffee, Lardy Cake and home made cake. Gourmet Tea comprises tea or coffee, along with assorted sandwiches, scone, butter, jam and cream and home made cake. Bread, cakes, scones and jams are home made with traditional teabreads, rich farm milk and cream and delicious Devon ice cream. Teas include Assam, Darjeeling and Earl Grey.

Closed: Mondays and Tuesdays during summer, and the months of January and February.

MAIDSTONE   **Kent**

Elizabeth's Tea Room
8 Pudding Lane   Parking 50m.
Maidstone
01622 674588

Elizabeth's Tea Room is a Tudor building. Tastefully decorated and homely, with smoking (with fans) and non-smoking areas, waitress service brings tea in china pots and cups.

Afternoon Tea and Cream Tea serve either a pot of tea with two scones, jam and cream, or substitute a slice of cake for one of the scones. Bread, scones and cakes are all home baked and there is a good selection. Scones include cheese, fruit, date and walnut and cherry and almond. Cream Teas are available all day long, and among the teas in the pot are Assam, Ceylon, China, Darjeeling and Earl Grey.

Closed: Sundays.

MATFIELD

Cherry Trees Tea Gallery
The Green   Disabled Access
Matfield   Parking on site
Nr. Tonbridge
01892 722187

Cherry Trees Tea Gallery is also the Post Office on the Village Green opposite the pond. The early 16th century building contains many items of interest to its visitors, including a pianola, on which guests can play to receive "certificates of achievement", and a collection of advertising memorabilia spread over three rooms. The gardens cover an acre, with much to watch and admire. In fine weather, tea is taken in the garden.

Home made scones, fresh cream, jam and home made cakes provide a very adequate repast, or there are special recipe toasted teacakes and a choice of cake. Cakes, scones and jams are home made, with a selection of teas including Assam, Ceylon, China, Darjeeling and Earl Grey.

Closed: Wednesday afternoons in winter season.

Fir Tree House Tea Rooms
Fir Tree House   Disabled Access
Penshurst
01892 870382

The Fir House Tea Rooms are set in the centre of the village, next to the village hall, and close to the vineyards in a delightful Tudor building with inglenook fireplace, polished floors and lovely atmosphere. The pretty cottage garden is open in summer and has won the "Best Afternoon Tea Competition" run by the tourist authority.

Tea and scones with cream and jam, or tea and cakes are on offer, or Set Afternoon Tea offers a combination of both, with a slice of granary bread and tea or coffee. All the food is baked on the premises by the proprietor, Caroline Fuller-Rowell. Herbal and fruit teas join old favourites Ceylon, China, Darjeeling, Earl Grey and Lapsang Souchong.

Closed: Mondays, and November and December.

Quaintways Tearooms
High Street   Disabled Access
Penshurst   Parking 50m.
01892 870272

Situated in the centre of the historic village, Quaintways Tearooms is close to Penshurst Place and vineyards.

With a wealth of beams, the rear tearoom is a converted bakehouse, retaining its Victorian oven. The premises are shared by a gift shop and antique showroom.

Quaintways Cream Tea consists of two home made scones with butter, cream and jam, with a choice of tea or coffee. The Plain Tea comes without the cream. Cakes and scones are home baked with home made tea breads and local untreated cream.

There is a large selection of fruit and herbal teas as well as the ever popular Assam, Ceylon, China, Darjeeling and Earl Grey.

The Cobtree Tearooms

The Museum of Kent Life
Cobtree
Lock Lane
Sandling
Nr. Maidstone
01622 663708 / 763936

Disabled Access
Parking on site

Housed in the Museum of Kent Life, the Tearooms are part of the visitor services at the museum. Providing quality home made fare in the farmhouse building, proprietor Mary Bonner is pleased to offer Cobtree Cream Tea to weary visitors, comprising a pot of tea for one, two home made scones, strawberry jam and whipped cream. Orchard Afternoon Tea gives a pot of tea, two apple and cheese scones served with butter, an apple and a slice of cheese. Cakes and scones are home baked, and the teas available include Assam, Ceylon, China, Darjeeling and Earl Grey.

Closed: End October to April 1st.

SANDWICH

Cherubs

8 Potter Street
Sandwich
01304 614805

Disabled Access
Parking 100m.

Set off the High Street in a side road of the historic town that is home to many antique shops, Cherub's was built about 1640.

As might be expected, the interior theme is cherubs accompanying the delicacies to be sampled. Tea consists of a sandwich of the customer's choice, a scone with jam and cream, a slice of cake and a pot of tea or coffee. Cakes, scones and jams are all home made and there is a good selection of teas such as Assam, Ceylon, China, Darjeeling and Earl Grey.

Closed: Sundays during winter season.

Little Cottage Tearooms

The Quay

Sandwich

01304 614387

Disabled Access

Parking 50m.

Little Cottage Tearooms can be found by the River Stour on the quay by the Barbican. The old cottage has two foot thick walls, decorated in pale pink, with pink tablecloths and lace covers. Smoking is upstairs only, apart from Sundays. Proprietor Susan Wendholt holds three Clean Food awards and the Healthy Heart award.

Tea allows guests to choose the bread for their sandwich as well as its filling. A scone with butter, jam and cream follows, with home made cake and a cup of tea, very reasonably priced. The Cream Tea offers the scones and tea option. Bread, scones and cakes are all home made and a good selection of teas include Assam, Darjeeling and Earl Grey.

Closed: Mondays and Fridays.

STOWTING

Oak Tree Farm Tearooms

Stowting

Nr. Ashford

01233 750297

Disabled Access

Parking on site

Set in a secluded community area close to Lyminge Forest, with breathtaking views of the countryside, Oak Tree Farm Tearooms is an attractive venue for tea.

In season customers use the garden with its patio, enjoying the sumptuous fare on offer. With no set menu, there is plenty of choice with lemon meringue pie, chocolate torte, pavlova and bara brith among the delicacies available. Cakes and scones are home made, and cream teas are popular with guests. Assam, Darjeeling and Earl Grey are some of the teas in the pot.

Closed: Mondays, and January and February.

TEYNHAM   Kent

Cherry Tree Tea Room
90 London Road   Parking opposite
Teynham
Nr. Sittingbourne
01795 522855

Near to the Swan Inn and opposite the library and antique shop, Cherry
Tree Tea Room is near places of interest such as Brogdale Research (fruit)
Farm, Syndale Vineyard, the Barge Museum and Chatham Historical Dock-
yard.

Proprietor David Jackson Grant is enthusiastic about the food in his tea
room. Cream Tea features fresh Jersey cream with a home made scone,
butter and a choice of jam. Locally made gateaux galore, Winters Fresh
Jersey Herd Ice Cream and freshly ground coffee of several types are some
of the other attractions, with teas on offer being Assam, Ceylon, Darjeeling
and Earl Grey. There is a craft shop attached to the tea room to further the
enjoyment and interest of visitors.

Closed: Sundays during winter season.

WEST MALLING

The Old Mill Tea Room
Mill Yard Craft Centre   Parking 50m.
Swan Street
West Malling
01732 844311

Mill Yard Craft Centre is beside the Post Office in Swan Street and local
attractions include Manor Park and St. Leonard's Tower. The Old Mill Tea
Room is situated within the historic olde worlde craft centre and provides a
relaxed and traditional atmosphere.

Cream Tea serves a warm scone with jam and cream and a pot of tea, and
there is a wide selection of tray bakes and home made cakes. Among the
teas are Assam, Darjeeling and Earl Grey.

Closed: Sundays during winter season.

CHORLEY   Lancashire

Muffins
5 Fazakerley Street   Disabled Access
Chorley
01257 262566

Established 1974, Muffins is a good place of refuge after visiting the market; Tuesday is the busiest and is known locally as the "Flat Iron". Inside, two Welsh dressers feature home made cakes, takeaway loaves and a few calico plates.

With no set menu there is plenty to choose from the wide range of hot puddings, such as sticky toffee, or fridge cakes like coffee renoirs. Banana cream pies, vegan flapjacks and malt loaf team up with rarities like Parsnip Passion Cake, and of course there is a choice of muffins. Children and vegetarians are catered for, with bread, cakes and scones all home baked. Teas include Assam, Ceylon, Darjeeling, Earl Grey and Lapsang Souchong as well as fruit and herbal varieties and many other hot beverages.

Closed: Sundays.

DARWEN

Marjory's Tea Room
65 Blackburn Road   Parking 50m.
Darwen
01254 776587

A cosy atmosphere and friendly service is offered by proprietor Marjory Harrison to all her customers, who might also enjoy a browse around her husband's secondhand/antique shop downstairs.

Cakes and scones are all home baked, and no set menu allows for a greater choice among the very reasonably priced goodies. Freshly cut sandwiches and special toasties tempt those who prefer their savouries, and traditional scones with jam and cream are available for the sweet-toothed. Earl Grey is the favourite tea on offer.

Closed: Sundays and Mondays.

FLEETWOOD   **Lancashire**

Lantern Tea Rooms
30 Kent Road   Disabled Access
Fleetwood   Parking in street
01253 874418

Lantern Tea Rooms sits alongside the tramtracks from Fleetwood to Blackpool
and close to Fleetwood Market, a lovely promenade and the Isle of Man Ferry.
The tea rooms are set in an old building with seating for about thirty outside
on the patio in front during good weather.
Afternoon Tea offers a toasted teacake, a scone with jam and cream and a pot
of tea per person. Cakes and scones are all home baked and there is a good
selection to choose from, including fruit pies and egg custards. Among the
teas available are Assam, Ceylon, China, Darjeeling and Earl Grey.

Closed: Wednesdays.

GREAT MITTON

Hillcrest Tea Rooms
Great Mitton   Disabled Access
Nr. Clitheroe   Parking on site
01254 826573

Hillcrest Tea Rooms are set in a small hamlet next to the mediaeval church,
and not far from famous public school, Stoneyhurst College.
The old building has a cheerful atmosphere with friendly staff serving at
lace tablecloths. Scones, cakes and jams are all home made and there is no
set menu, to allow for a wider choice amongst the customers. Parkin is
among the house specialities, and the range of teas include Assam, China,
Darjeeling and Earl Grey.

Closed: Fridays, and the Christmas period and January.

RIBCHESTER   Lancashire

The Village Tea Shop
20 Water Street   Disabled Access
Ribchester   Parking 100m.
Nr. Preston
01254 878297

The stone-built village house is furnished with beechwood and pine, with Laura Ashley table coverings and an abundance of plants. Tea provides a choice of sandwich, a scone with jam and butter, a cake from the daily display and a choice of tea. Child's Tea offers jam, honey or peanut butter sandwich, with a glass of milk and Dolly Mixtures. Scones and cakes are home made and bread is baked locally. Six types of ground coffee are served in cafetieres with decaffeinated and among the teas are Assam, Ceylon, China, Darjeeling and Earl Grey.

Closed: Mondays and Tuesdays (except Bank Holidays), and weekdays between January and Easter.

WHALLEY

Toby Jug Tea Shop
20 King Street   Disabled Access
Whalley   Parking on site
Nr. Clitheroe
01254 823298

Toby Jug Tea Shop is a 300 year old listed building in a conservation area, one of the oldest properties in the village. Oak beams and upstairs panelling, believed to have come from the Abbey itself is evidence of its antiquity. Old stone fireplaces add to the atmosphere.
Cream Tea offers a scone, jam, whipped cream and pot of Yorkshire Tea or cup of Peaberry Coffee. Country Tea adds to that a slice of delicious home made cake and the Traditional English Tea serves a cucumber or tomato sandwich and tea or coffee. Pure dairy ice cream is available and the wide range of teas includes Assam, Ceylon, China, Darjeeling and Earl Grey.

Closed: Mondays and Tuesdays.

The Chatteries Tea Rooms

7 Jaxon Court   Parking 50m.
Hallgate
Wigan
01942 820988

The Chatteries are part of an olde worlde complex to the side of Wigan bus station, where visitors can take a look at local heritage. They are not far from the famous Wigan Pier.

Menus include the cream tea, which offers a scone with cream and preserve and a pot of English Breakfast Tea. A hungry customer dines on hot pot with red cabbage or beetroot, a pot of tea or coffee and a scone or eccles cake. Cakes are all home baked and there is a good choice of teas including Assam, Ceylon, Darjeeling and Earl Grey.

Closed: Sundays, and the Christmas period.

-------0-------

Nasturtium Leaf Sandwiches

Spread Anchovy paste sparingly. Add shredded Nasturtium leaves.

(Five O' Clock Tea, 1886)

The Tudor Court Tea Rooms

51A Market Street   Disabled Access
Ashby de la Zouch   Parking 50m.
01530 417610

Situated in the middle of Market Street behind a Tudor building, The Tudor Court Tea Rooms are aptly named. The building is said to be the second oldest in Ashby. An uncovered wall inside is believed to date back to the fifteenth century. In front of the tea room is a beautiful courtyard where guests can sit in the summer.

Scones, cakes and jams are all home made. Tea is served with a scone, jam and cream, or assorted sandwiches (salmon, cheese, beef or ham) come with a scone, jam and cream, home made cake with cream and a choice of tea. Teas on offer include Assam, Ceylon, China, Darjeeling and Earl Grey.

BOSTON

Naughty's Tea-Shoppe

38B Dolphin Lane   Parking 50m.
Boston
01205 363961

Near to Pump Square, the tea shop is also local to the Boston Stump and Windmill, Blackfriars Theatre and the River Witham.

The site is small, but proprietor Mandy Chambers believes that for such a small venue there is a very big atmosphere. Inside, the shelves are arrayed with a large collection of teapots and local artists display their work on the walls.

Cakes and scones are home made and there is no set menu, so that visitors can choose for themselves from the selection of toasted teacakes, oozing with butter, or the scones with fresh double cream and jam. Among the teas are Assam, Darjeeling and Earl Grey.

Closed: Sundays.

LUTTERWORTH

Roseannes

Van Allen Court
27 Market Street
Lutterworth
01455 552212

Disabled Access
Parking on site

Found opposite the Co-op, Roseannes is close to the church made famous by John Wycliffe. On Thursdays there is a market. Living up to the name, roses feature in the decor, with rose china and border. There is also an unusual collection of teapots which add to the character of the tea room.

There is no set menu, which allows greater freedom of choice for the guest. Cakes, scones and jams are all home made and very reasonably priced. Among the teas in the pot are Assam, Ceylon, China, Darjeeling and Earl Grey.

Closed: Sundays (open by request).

WISTOW

Wistow Tea Rooms

Wistow Garden Centre
Wistow
Nr. Great Glen
01162 593756

Disabled Access
Parking on site

Wistow Tea Rooms are set in the heart of the country, on a three thousand acre private estate and share a site with craft shops, an artists studio, farm shop and garden and aquatic centre.

Cream Teas offer a pot of tea with two home made scones, jam and a choice of clotted or whipped cream. Or there are sandwiches and a scone with all the trimmings. Bread, cakes, scones and jams are all home made and all the water used in cooking or for drinks is from fresh spring fed wells, which means that the tea rooms have three times been the winner of the Tea Councils Award for Excellence for the best cup of Tea in the U.K. Teas include Assam, Darjeeling and Earl Grey.

FLEET HARGATE

Willow Tea Rooms
Old Maine Road
Fleet Hargate
Nr. Spalding
01406 423112

Disabled Access
Parking on site

The hundred and fifty year old building is prettily decorated in blue and yellow, with willow pattern crockery. Large, sunny windows make up for times when the weather is not good enough to sit on the patio.

High Tea consists of a round of sandwiches or a roll with a piece of fruit cake, sponge or scone and a pot of tea. Cream Tea offers two scones with jam and cream and a pot of tea. Bread, cakes and scones are home baked and those who like to play safe will enjoy a cup of P.G.Tips, whilst the more adventurous might like to try Earl Grey.

Closed: Mondays.

GRANTHAM

Conduit Tea Gardens
3 Conduit Lane
The Market Place
Grantham
01476 71907

Disabled Access
Parking 50m.

Set in the quiet corner of the Market Square, Conduit Tea Gardens overlook the old conduit used by the Greyfriars since 1365. Last year a hoard of old groats and half groats were found when a new water metre was installed. It is now at the British Museum.

Poached egg on toast with a scone and cream and tea is one of the choices on the menu. For small parties, a tea including sandwiches can be laid on if given twenty four hours notice. Cakes, scones and some of the jams are home made, the cakes especially enjoying a good local reputation, with carrot, chocolate mayonnaise, apple curd and apricot and a whole range of delicious cheesecakes in various tantalising flavours. Teas include Assam, Ceylon, China, Darjeeling and Earl Grey.

Closed: Sundays.

LINCOLN

Lincoln Cathedral Coffee Shop

Lincoln Cathedral
Lincoln
01522 544544

Disabled Access
Parking 100m.

Situated just off the cloisters in the cathedral under the library, the coffee shop is also not far from Lincoln Castle, the Museum and the historic Bailgate. Food and drink can be taken outside onto Tennyson Green where seating is available around the statue of Lord Tennyson. In the summer there is also seating in the Mediaeval cloisters.

Cakes and scones are home baked and there is a wide selection of drinks including hot chocolate, cappuccino coffee or sparkling elderflower. Teas available include Assam, Ceylon, Darjeeling and Earl Grey.

Closed: Sundays.

MARKET RASEN

Wickentree Coffee and Tea Shop

Caistor Road
Market Rasen
01067 384218

Disabled Access
Parking on site

Situated on the edge of the Lincolnshire wolds, the tea shop is close to horse racing, golf, rambling, horse riding and fishing and provides good refreshment after such activities.

Part of renovated farm buildings, with timber beams and pine furniture to give an olde worlde effect, it is possible to buy hand carved or pine furniture on site. Jams and pickles are also for sale as are garden ornaments.

Tea furnishes a pot of tea, assorted sandwiches and cakes or scones and jam. Bread, cakes, scones and jam are all home made, and teas include Assam, Ceylon, China, Darjeeling and Earl Grey.

Closed: January.

Melrose Tea Room

Broadway Centre
The Broadway
Woodhall Spa
01526 35384

Disabled Access
Parking 50m.

Customers of the Melrose Tea Room agree that it is a good place to meet, and it is a favourite haunt of local people. Gillian Mueller is the proprietor, who offers a very reasonably priced Afternoon Tea to her guests. This comprises a sandwich, scone, cream and jam, cake or pie and pot of tea. The customer has a choice of all of the component parts right down to the type of bread used in the sandwich, making healthy options possible. Cream Tea provides a scone with cream, jam and a pot of tea. Cakes and scones are home baked, and the teas in the pot include Assam and Earl Grey.

Closed: Wednesdays during January and February only.

STAMFORD

Frangipani Tea Room

3 Red Lion Square
Stamford
01780 62422

Parking 50m.

Frangipani Tea rooms is set in the picturesque town of Stamford, within fifty yards of the doctor's house as filmed for the television version of Middlemarch. The tea rooms are also within easy reach of Burghley House, where The Buccaneers was filmed. In 1934, the site was a very popular tea room. Tables are covered with French cloths and there is a display of local artists' work. A varied menu offers home made cakes and, time permitting, staff are willing to prepare an item for a customer if it is not on the menu. In case guests are unable to finish the generous portions, leftovers can be wrapped to take home (doggy bag service). Earl Grey is the favourite tea.

Closed: Sundays and public holidays.

The George Hotel
High Street   Disabled Access
St. Martins   Parking on site
Nr. Stamford
01780 55171

The George Hotel is close to Burghley House, historic Stamford Town and
the Nene Valley Railway.
During the winter, tea may be taken in the lounge area in front of a blazing log
fire. In summer, the cobbled courtyard, decorated with hanging baskets, is the
ideal venue.
Afternoon Tea offers two scones with Cornish clotted cream and jam, or fruit
cake and chocolate sponge cake. All cakes and scones are freshly home baked,
and among the teas available are Assam, Ceylon, China, Darjeeling and Earl
Grey. There is also a choice of soft drinks.

--------0-------

*Tea, though ridiculed by those who are naturally coarse in their
nervous sensibilities... will always be the favourite beverage of the
intellectual.*

(Thomas de Quincey - Confessions of an English Opium Eater)

BATTERSEA

The Gallery Tearooms
103 Lavender Hill   Disabled Access
Battersea   Parking on site
0171 350 2564

The Gallery Tearooms are close to Clapham Junction and Common and near to Battersea Park and Arts Centre.

With background classical music and opera, the tearooms have an Edwardian salon setting, with chandeliers, paintings, tapestries and high ceilings, giving a spacious feel. Vintage china is used and silver plated cutlery. One conversation piece is the old sofa with stuffed toys donated by customers, which have been in many international magazines. It is often used as a venue for film sets and fashion shoots.

CROUCH END

Wisteria Tea Rooms
14 Middle Lane   Disabled Access
Crouch End
0181 348 2669

Two hundred yards from the Clock Tower and within easy reach of Alexandra Palace, Wisteria Tea Rooms is totally non-smoking, including the garden which is open seasonally, weather permitting. The decor is Victorian/Edwardian featuring many Loom chairs and tables with antiques and bric-a-brac for decoration and sale. The crockery and cutlery is old, mismatched and beautiful. Background music is mostly classical and light.

Cream Teas bring two scones, double cream, jam and a pot of tea. High Tea comprises a choice of sandwich, piece of cake (non cream) and a pot of tea or cafetiere of coffee. All scones and cakes are home baked, using free range eggs. Jams are also home made and there is a wide selection of other goodies to choose from. Teas are all loose leaf and feature among their number Assam, Ceylon, China, Darjeeling and Earl Grey.

Closed: Mondays.

Stravinsky's Russian Tea House
6 Fulham High Street
Fulham
0171 371 0001

Disabled Access
Parking 50m.

Stravinsky's Russian Tea House is the only Russian style tea house in London, importing products from the former U.S.S.R. Managing   Director, David Fanailov hails from Azerbaijan and has created a superb atmosphere with the stark furnishings and bare wood floors. Guests enjoy a choice of twenty five types of tea as they listen to the classical and church background music. Teas are served in special glasses that are kept warm on trivets and are available for sale.

Cream Tea offers two scones with clotted cream, jam and any tea or coffee. High Tea is also available and there is a wide range of sandwiches with exotic fillings such as lettuce and mint or date and pistachio. Bread, cakes, scones and jams are all home made and specialities include poppy seed strudel, Russian cheesecake and charlotte Malakov.

GREENWICH

Peter de Wit
21 Greenwich Church Street
Greenwich
0181 305 0048

Disabled Access
Parking 50m.

The building is listed, dating from 1707, its Tudor back, dating from 1580. Proprietor Peter de Wit has cultivated a very relaxed atmosphere attracting a young and friendly clientele. White bone china and a curious collection of chairs and tables create the decor, in addition to a variety of hand made wooden objects, which are for sale.

Cream Teas offer a large scone, jam, Cornish cream (as used by the Ritz) and a pot of tea or other beverage. Peter specialises in traditional cakes and pastries, which are all home made. Sandwiches are made to the individual guest's requirements. The wide range of teas includes Assam, Ceylon, China, Darjeeling and Earl Grey.

The Tea House
14 King William's Walk
Greenwich
0181 858 0803

Disabled Access
Parking 100m.

The Tea House is 18th century, with panelled walls and two large fires. There is a large bay, panelled glass window, and pine floorboards and furniture give a traditional feel. Outside there is a tea garden.

Afternoon Tea offers a choice of tea or coffee from the menu, a sandwich and cake, each of the customer's choice. Cream Tea comprises tea or coffee, two sultana scones, Devon clotted cream and strawberry jam. Bread, cakes, scones and jams are all home baked, with traditional teacakes amongst the fare.

There is a large range of teas and coffees, the former including Assam, Ceylon, China, Darjeeling and Earl Grey, coffees including chocolate marshmallow and Grand Marnier.

HAMPSTEAD

Hampstead Tea Rooms
9 South End Road
Hampstead
0171 435 9563

Close to Hampstead Heath and Keat's house, the Hampstead Tea Rooms is ideal for walkers on the Heath.

The friendly atmosphere, with tables outside in season, the Tea Time Special offers mixed sandwiches, any fresh cream cake and tea or coffee.

There are so many specialities, only visiting and sampling will do justice to the list which includes strawberry tarts, cheesecakes, Danish pastries, a variety of breads, savoury strudels and bagels with assorted fillings. Teas include Darjeeling and Earl Grey as well as herbal and fruit infusions and there is a good selection of coffee.

Oak Room Tea Lounge, Le Meridien

21 Piccadilly   Disabled Access

0171 734 8000 Ext. 2309   Parking 400m.

Le Meridien offers modern luxury, tradition and charm to its guests. The Oak Room Tea Lounge has been restored to its former Edwardian glory. Formal, but unstuffy, the soothing elegance of the oak panelled room is augmented by comfortable armchairs and background music by a harpist. Service is efficient and discreet.

The speciality is English Afternoon Tea, typically comprising a quartet of Tea sandwiches, home made scones and pastries. There is a good selection of teas, including Assam, Ceylon, Darjeeling, Earl Grey, Jasmine and Lapsang Souchong.

PIMLICO

Elliotts Tea and Coffee Room

76 Tachbrook Street   Parking 50m.

Pimlico

0171 932 0717

Two minutes from Tachbrook Street Market and close to the Tate Gallery, Elliott's is the only Tea and coffee house of its kind in Central London, offering a relaxing oasis amidst the bustling Pimlico Market, and an imaginative menu. The decor upstairs is black and white,   downstairs has a parlour kitchen atmosphere.

Afternoon teas are realistically priced, with Cream Tea offering scones, clotted cream, jam and a pot of tea. High Tea consists of Assorted sandwiches, buns, cakes and a pot of tea.

Proprietor and cook Simon Barrett recommends the banoffi pie as his favourite speciality, and would even go so far as to say it's the best in London. Bread, cakes, scones and jam are all home made and the selection of teas includes Assam, Ceylon, China, Darjeeling, Earl Grey and English Breakfast.

Closed: Sundays during winter season.

Dormouse Tea Room

4 Greenbank Road   Parking 50m.
Mossley Hill
Liverpool
0151 733 7425

Inside, old fashioned cosy decor provides a peaceful atmosphere for a smoke and a bite to eat whilst waited on by uniformed waitress service. Lewis Carroll's Dormouse would have loved it here! Set Tea offers a choice of sandwich, a scone with jam and cream and tea. Cakes are home made and speciality tea and coffee by Taylors of Harrogate are available, among them, Assam, Ceylon, Darjeeling and Earl Grey.

Closed: Sundays.

SOUTHPORT

Nostalgia Tea Rooms

215-217 Lord Street   Parking 50m.
Southport
01704 501294

Nostalgia by name and nature, the building which houses the Tea Rooms was built in 1905 in half-timbered black and white style. Inside is a distinctive peach and green decor, with personally designed, matching tables and chairs. Full china crockery is brought to the tables by traditionally clad waitresses. Proprietor Ann Couzens is pleased hers was a founder member of the Tea Council Guild of Tea Shops.
Afternoon Tea serves a plate of the day's selected sandwiches, a cake with cream and a pot of tea for one or a cup of coffee. The Nostalgia Special presents a selection of both smoked salmon and cucumber sandwiches, the cake and choice of beverage. Specialities include the gateaux in an attractive display and cinnamon toast and crumpets with Maple Syrup and cream. Thirst-quenchers include Assam, Ceylon, Darjeeling and Earl Grey.

Closed: Mondays (except in high summer).

Mr. Pickwick's Tea Room

Brookfarm   Disabled Access
Stoneleigh Road   Parking on site
Coventry
01203 693547

Located on the road to the university and handy for Christmas tree sales in
winter and fruit-picking in summer, Mr. Pickwick's Tea Room is housed in a
converted tractor shed on a fruit-picking farm, set beside a brook with a
waterfall. Inside, olde worlde decor with wooden beams, hops, a tiled floor
and pine furniture brings back memories of a bygone age. Pictures from
Dickens' Pickwick Papers adorn the walls.

Afternoon Tea comprises a scone with jam and cream, a slice of fruit cake and
tea for one or strawberries and cream accompany the scone. There are various
combinations, with home made cakes and scones tempting the customer.
Specialities include apple cakes and pies, carrot cakes and bread and butter
pudding. Among the teas are Assam, Ceylon, China, Darjeeling and Earl Grey.

LITTLE CORNBOW

Cornbow Manna Coffee Shop

Zion Christian Centre   Disabled Access
Little Cornbow   Parking on site
Halesowen
0121 585 5103

Next to the Health Centre and opposite the swimming pool, Cornbow Manna
Coffee Shop is run by members of Zion Christian Centre and local churches
on a voluntary basis. Service is friendly and economical with a small Christian
bookshop attached. The paintings on the walls are all by local artists. There is
no set menu, but a good variety of home made cakes, scones and apple pie
ensures a tempting repast for the weary customer. Filter coffee and herbal teas
wash the meal down.

Closed: Sundays, Christmas week and Easter weekend.

Willow Tree Tea Rooms

1 Bridgnorth Road   Parking on site
Stourton
Stourbridge
01384 873555

Surrounded by beautiful countryside with canal walks nearby and the Black Country Crystal Glass Works to be visited, Willow Tree Tea Rooms is decorated in 1930s style and with its open fire provides a welcome rest for weary travellers.

Cream Tea consists of a scone with jam and cream and a pot of tea, while cheese on toast comes with a cake or scone and a pot of tea. Traditional home made puddings are the speciality here. Bread and butter pudding vies with treacle tart and lemon meringue for orders. Cakes and scones are also home made, while the crusty bread is baked locally. Teas include Ceylon, Darjeeling, Earl Grey, English Breakfast and Lemon.

Closed: two weeks at end of February.

SUTTON COLDFIELD

Hungry Horse Tea Room

Hungry Horse Craft Centre   Parking on site
Weeford Road
Sutton Coldfield
0121 323 3658

Close to Sutton Park, the Hungry Horse Tea Room is set in beautiful country, with views of the horses in the fields. The old farmhouse has a friendly atmosphere with an outside patio which is used in summer. Children are welcome to the healthy, Non-Smoking environment, which is apparently frequented by a ghost.

Cakes are home made and everything freshly prepared. There is no set menu, but an assortment of individually priced goodies. Teas include Assam and Earl Grey.

Closed: Mondays.

Margaret's at Chestnut Farmhouse

The Street   Parking on site
Baconsthorpe
Nr. Holt
01263 577614

Margaret's is situated in the main street of the village of Baconsthorpe. Lace tablecloths and a winter time log burner contribute to the homely atmosphere, as does the No Smoking policy. Proprietors Margaret and Roger Bacon are Heartbeat Award winners. Cakes, pastries, scones, bread and jam are baked by Margaret in the farmhouse kitchen. Cream Tea offers two scones, with jam and fresh cream and tea. Muffin Tea comprises toasted muffin with butter and jam or honey, a portion of cake chosen from the Pembroke table. Teas include Assam, Ceylon, Darjeeling and Earl Grey.

Closed: Mondays (except during high summer) and November to March (except for private bookings).

CLEY-NEXT-THE-SEA

Whalebone House

High Street   Disabled Access
Cley-next-the-Sea   Parking 100m.
Nr. Holt
01263 740336

Whalebone House is a Grade II listed building with decorative bone work and flints. Inside are traditional 1920s decor and music. Attention to detail, personal service and the highest quality food available, using local produce wherever available, has won proprietors Selena and Stuart Bragg a "Partnership Award" from the local council.
Tea serves egg or cucumber sandwiches, a scone with jam and cream and a pot of tea. Cakes and scones are home baked on the premises, as is the bread, made from locally grown and milled wheat. Specialities include Banoffi pie and strawberries and cream.

Closed: Mondays (except Bank Holidays).

Garden Tearoom and Country Gifts

24C Norwich Street
Dereham
01362 691138

Disabled Access
Parking 50m.

Set in the second largest town in Norfolk, the Garden Tearoom is well located for visitors to see Bishop Bonner's cottage, the Rural Life Museum and St. Withburga's Well. The typically English tearoom revels in lace tablecloths and china cups and saucers, but could not be described as stuffy, providing high chairs on request. Gifts, china and pictures are for sale in the gift shop, and a No Smoking policy makes this a healthy environment in which to take tea. Bread, cakes and scones are freshly prepared and cooked on the premises. Teas in the pot include Darjeeling and Earl Grey.

Closed: Sundays.

HEACHAM

Norfolk Lavender LTD./ Miller's Cottage Tea Room

Caley Mill
Heacham
Nr. Kings Lynn
01485 571965

Disabled Access
Parking 50m.

Built in the mid-1800s as a water powered grain mill, beamed ceilings bring back the old days when the miller lived here. In summer months lavender sprigged curtains contrast with the dark wood furniture, and guests can sit outside on the patio to take tea. The olde worlde theme is continued in the menu which offers Lavender Tea, a blend of China and Darjeeling with a Norfolk lavender, providing a refreshing and relaxing beverage, with a lavender scone or lavender lemon sponge.

Bread, scones, cakes, jams, pastries, flans, marmalades and chutneys - all are home made and packaged in the kitchens on site and are available for sale in the Carrstone Mill gift shop adjoining, to remind guests of the delicious flavours they enjoyed at tea. A wide choice of teas are on offer.

The Owl Tea Rooms

White Lion Street
Holt
01263 713232

Disabled Access
Parking 100m.

The Owl Tea Rooms can be found at the end of the High Street and on the corner with Church Street.

The Georgian listed building has a baker in the front and the tea room to the rear. Inside, pews from the methodist chapel complement the hand thrown tableware, made by the owners, Patricia and Terence Hulbert, who are as proud of their waitress service as they are of the food. Outside a walled cottage garden allows eating al fresco on summer days.

Cream Tea consists of a fruit scone with jam, cream and a pot of tea, for £1.95. Alternatively, brown bread and butter, jam, a choice of cake and a pot of tea cost £2.00. Bread, cakes, scones and jams are all home made on the premises. Chocolate fudge cake and biscuits rank among the specialities on offer, and the choice of teas include Assam, Ceylon, China, Darjeeling and Earl Grey.

Closed: Sundays and all Bank Holidays.

-------0-------

Retired to their tea and scandal,
according to their ancient custom.

(William Congreve)

Tudor Tea Rooms

4 Norwich Road
Fakenham
01328 851225

Disabled Access
Parking 100m.

The Grade II Listed building is small, simple, clean and homely and welcomes well-behaved children of all ages. A local artist displays local scenes on the walls. Tea comprises a sardine and tomato sandwich, gateaux and cream, coffee and refill. Cakes and scones are home made, specialities including treacle tart, bread pudding and toasted teacakes, along with the freshly made sandwiches. On Saturdays after 2.30pm, tea or coffee can be enjoyed with a choice of gateau, scone, apple pie or sausage roll. Among the teas available are Assam and Earl Grey.

Closed: Sundays all year, and Wednesday afternoons in winter.

NORTH WALSHAM

Butterfingers

1 Mitre Tavern Yard
North Walsham
01692 500642

Disabled Access
Parking 100m.

Butterfingers is towards the bottom of town, next to Blakeman's carpets. It is within visiting distance of the cat pottery, Norfolk's Motor Cycle Museum and various historic buildings in the town. The small listed building has original decor, with wooden tables and chairs on a stone floor and historic photographs depicting North Walsham's past. Framed photographs are available for purchase. Proprietors Mark and Maureen Whewell hold the Heartbeat Award for healthy eating, although the Cream Tea is delightfully decadent, comprising two fruit scones, with butter, jam and cream and a choice of tea.
Cakes are home made, the main speciality being a cake that is good for you. Guinness cake is a moist fruit cake made with the beer. Teas include Assam, Ceylon, China, Darjeeling and Earl Grey.

Closed: Sundays and Wednesday afternoons.

June's Coffee Shop

Taverham Nursery Centre   Disabled Access
Fir Covet Road   Parking on site
Norwich
01603 861530

June's Coffee Shop is situated in the middle of a very large garden centre, which has a Fish house, flower centre and walk round plant gardens.
There is no set menu, customers having a choice of order from the range of home baked bread, cakes and scones.

Closed: Christmas period.

THETFORD

Time for Tea

10 Bridge Street   Disabled Access
Thetford   Parking 100m.
Norfolk
01842 766234

Time for Tea has two separate rooms, front Non-Smoking, and a courtyard for warmer months. Coach parties are welcome and highchairs are available for those with small children.
There is a variety of home baked cakes and scones, pies and pastries for visitors to choose from.

Closed: Wednesday afternoons.

Holkham Hall Tearooms
Wells-next-the-Sea   Disabled Access
01328 710227   Parking on site

Set in the grounds of Holkham Hall, the tearooms are also close to the pottery
and museum. In warm weather, tea may be taken on the lawn.
Bread, cakes, scones and jams are all home made, many baked on the premises.
Proprietor Brigitta Crewe recommends the apple pie as a speciality. Teas in
the pot include Earl Grey, fruit and herbal varieties.

Closed: Fridays and Saturdays, and between October and Easter.

-------0-------

Soft yielding minds to water glide away
And sip, with Nymphs, their elemental tea.

(Alexander Pope - Rape of the Lock)

GEDDINGTON

Eleanor House Restaurant and Tea Shop

Eleanor Cross
Geddington
01536 742266

Disabled Access
Parking on site

Facing Eleanor Cross, which was built 1294, in the centre of the village, Eleanor House was built about 1650 and is close to Boughton House, the English Versailles. The tea rooms enjoy an intimate, informal atmosphere with polished pine tables and old elm chairs. Fine bone china such as Aynsley and Wedgewood adds a touch of class.

Cream Tea serves up freshly baked hot scones with Derbyshire clotted cream and strawberry jam. Customers are free to choose from the extensive list of goodies, which include rich fruit and spiced teacakes, bread and butter pudding and meringues with clotted cream and fruit sauce. Special sandwiches are made to order. Bread, cakes, scones and jams are all home baked, and the wide range of teas include Assam, Ceylon, China, Darjeeling and Earl Grey.

Closed: Mondays (except Bank Holidays).

HARLESTONE

Cottage Tearooms

Harlestone Heath Garden Centre
Harlestone Road
Harlestone
01604 581108

Disabled Access
Parking on site

Situated opposite Harlestone Firs and close to Althorpe House, Cottage Tearooms are inside the garden centre compound, with attractive views of the flowers and shrubs on sale.

Inside, the tea rooms are bright and cosy, with black painted beams. Local artists display their pictures on the walls.

There is no set menu, so that customers can choose from the selection of home made cakes and scones on offer. The main tea available is Earl Grey.

STOKE BRUERNE

The Old Chapel Tearoom
Chapel Lane
Stoke Bruerne
Nr. Towcester
01604 863284

Disabled Access
Parking on site

The main street of the village is the Grand Union Canal, fronted by attractive buildings, including the Canal Museum. Two hundred years of history lie adjacent to The Old Chapel Tearoom. The tea room's gardens are shared with "Old Chapel Workshops", a craft studio and gallery. Exhibitions of paintings, sculpture, textiles and other media are organised throughout the year.

Cream Teas consist of a pot of tea, scones, jam, butter and cream. Bread, cakes and scones are home made and can be matched by visitors with the selection of teas, which include, Assam, Ceylon, China, Darjeeling and Earl Grey.

Closed: Mondays from November to Easter.

WEEKLEY

Jessica's Tea Shop
38 Weekley Village
Nr. Kettering
01536 82312

Disabled Access
Parking in village

Situated between Kettering and Geddington, Jessica's Tea Shop is one mile from Boughton House. The thatched cottage was a nineteenth century bakehouse, set in a pretty thatched village with seventeenth century almshouse and school. Inside, the ovens are still intact.

Cakes and scones are home baked and customers can choose from the display, rather than from a set menu. Local farm ice cream is a treat, and the speciality teas include Earl Grey, Lapsang Souchong, Rose Pouchong, Darjeeling and Lemon. Various herbal and fruit teas are also available.

Closed: Wednesdays.

The Copper Kettle Tea Room

21 Front Street   Parking 100m.
Bamburgh
01668 214315

Set in the centre of the village, close to Bamburgh Castle and the long, unspoilt, sandy beach, The Copper Kettle Tea Room houses a shop selling a range of preserves, biscuits and confectionery. The 18th Century stone built cottage has unique oak panelling inside, depicting carved local scenes. Original oak beams display various items of antique copperware. As well as being a member of the prestigious Guild of Tea shops and Egon Ronay recommended, the tea room has an entry within the "Ash" publication of "Eat, Drink and Sleep Smoke Free", though smokers and dogs are welcome in the patio garden.

Tea comprises a toasted sandwich, chocolate cake and cream, with tea or coffee. Cakes, scones and jams are home made and house specials are banana and coconut cake, coffee and walnut and "Tigger Tart". Among the teas are Assam, Ceylon, China, Darjeeling and Earl Grey.

Closed: November to mid-March.

-------0-------

Thunder and Lightning Sandwiches

Spread the bread with golden syrup and cover with Devon cream.

(Five O' Clock Tea, 1886)

White House Restaurant
Parliament Terrace   Parking 50m.
Nottingham
01159 419033

The White House is situated near the Royal Hotel and within walking distance of Nottingham Castle and "Tales of Robin Hood". Rather than a set menu, all items are priced individually to allow greater freedom of choice, with cups of coffee or tea sold separately. Cakes and scones are home baked on the premises and there is a range of freshly roasted coffees to choose from as well as the teas, which include old favourites like Assam, Ceylon, China, Darjeeling and Earl Grey.

Closed: Sundays.

OLLERTON

Ollerton Watermill Teashop
Millside   Parking 50m.
Market Place
Ollerton
Nr. Newark
01623 824094

Situated opposite the War Memorial ground and near to Rufford Country Park and Sherwood Forest, the home of Robin Hood, the teashop is in an old watermill which has recently been restored. The entrance is at the back of the waterwheel, over the mill race, with a glass viewing panel. Splendid views over the river make this a delightful venue to relax in.
Cakes, scones and jams are all home made, so that there is plenty to choose from when compiling a cream tea. There is no set menu, but specialities include Bakewell tart and carrot cake, made to the cook's own recipe. Among the teas in the pot are Darjeeling and Earl Grey.

Closed: Mondays, and November to February.

ABINGDON   Oxfordshire

Miss Marples Tea Shoppe
29A Broad Street   Parking 100m.
Abingdon
01235 555630

Miss Marples' Tea Shoppe is close to the Museum and Leisure centre and located to the rear of Woolworths. A late Georgian building, kept and decorated in traditional old English tearoom style, there is nothing cloak and dagger about the goings on at the teashop. Inside, an oak panelled wall with a fireplace adds to the sense of history.

Tea for Two comes with two cakes, whilst a Cream Tea presents two scones, jam, cream and a pot of tea. Cakes, scones and pancakes are all home baked and there is a good choice of teas including Assam, China, Darjeeling and Earl Grey.

Closed: Sundays and Bank Holiday Mondays.

Poppies Tea Rooms
37 Stert Street   Disabled Access
Abingdon   Parking 100m.
01235 526660

Poppies is close to the Town Hall and Museum, the river and Abbey meadows, all places to see in Abingdon. The old building has oak beams and the decor is kept to look traditional. Central heating means that it is always warm. Two rooms cater for smokers and non-smokers and the service is friendly, polite and efficient. Food is always prepared to order in the fastest time possible.

Tea comprises a pot of tea for one, served with two freshly baked fruit scones, whipped cream and jam. Bread, cakes, scones and jam are home made and there is a vast choice to whet the appetite. Fruit cake, cherry sponge, date and walnut loaf, flapjack and shortbread are just some of the many delicacies available. There is also an extensive list of ice creams with flavours ranging from Bavarian black cherry and brown bread to chocolate trufito and white bombe. Teas include Assam, Ceylon, and Earl Grey.

Closed: Sundays.

CHIPPING NORTON   Oxfordshire

Annie's Country Pantry
22 New Street   Disabled Access
Chipping Norton   Parking 50m.
01608 641100

Annie's Country Pantry is close to such local attractions as the Museum, the
almshouses and Pool Meadow, a naturalist's haven. The tea room is in part of
an old house called Hill Lawn Manor. The main car park used to be the orchard
and the health centre was the swimming pool. Major Dunlop, the local vet,
lived in the Manor in 1920.
Edwardian Sandwich offers cake, a scone with butter and jam and a pot of tea
. Cakes, scones and jams are home made and bread from the local baker is
used in sandwiches. Earl Grey is the main tea on offer and fresh coffee is
always available.

Closed: Sundays during winter season.

GORING HEATH

Honeywood House
Goring Heath Post Office   Disabled Access
Goring Heath   Parking outside
01491 680200

Honeywood House is found inside the old Post Office, amidst wonderful
countryside, making it a popular resting point for walkers and cyclists. The
Victorian shop is quite unique, set as it is behind the shop area, with an open
fire and views of the garden which is quite safe for children and open for teas
in summer. The shop stocks flowers and groceries in addition to its speciality
chocolates and health foods.
Cream Tea consists of two home made scones with Jersey cream, jam and a
pot of tea. Cakes, scones and jams are all home made and on sale along with
pies, tarts and preserves in the shop. For the safe tea drinker, Tetley brew is
available, or there are various herbal teas, together with Assam and Earl Grey.

Closed: Mondays (except Bank Holidays).

HENLEY-ON-THAMES Oxfordshire

Crispins
Bridge House
52 Hart Street
Henley-on-Thames
01941 574232

Parking 50m.

Adjacent to Henley Bridge and overlooking the Thames, Bridge House is an elegant Georgian building, well-positioned for the Royal Regatta and boating activities all year round. Inside, potted palms and overmantel mirrors adorn the walls, creating an Edwardian ambience unique to Crispins. Proprietors Rodney and Edith Newbold offer personal, friendly and helpful service alongside their staff. Cream Tea provides hungry rowers with two home made scones, jam, butter and fresh cream, a pot of tea and a chocolate eclair. Cakes are all home baked, and specialities include meringues, apple pie and chocolate cake. A good selection of teas offers Assam, Ceylon, China, Darjeeling and Earl Grey.

Closed: Mondays (except Bank Holidays).

OXFORD

Convocation Coffee House
St. Mary's Church
High Street
Oxford
01865 794334

Disabled Access

Situated inside St. Mary's Church and conveniently placed for visits up the tower, the Convocation Coffee House is opposite Radcliffe Camera. The building dates from 1380 and boasts a vaulted ceiling which gives a spacious feel to the venue. A relaxed and happy atmosphere combines with the selection of food to provide a satisfactory eating place.
Cream teas come with home baked scones and cakes and the teas include Assam, Darjeeling and Earl Grey.

Closed: Good Friday.

Annies Tea Rooms
79 High Street
Wallingford
01491 836308

Disabled Access
Parking 50m.

The seventeenth century building has a clean, healthy environment, with a No Smoking policy throughout. The interior is a restful pale pink, with matching table coverings and china. There is a friendly and courteous waitress service. High Tea presents a pot of tea with two slices of bread and butter, home made jam and two cakes. Tea Cake Tea offers a pot of tea with two toasted teacakes and home made jam. Cakes, scones, jams and teacakes are all home baked, and an incredible range of over forty cakes is available. These include the date slice, featured by Woman and Home Magazine, Sunshine fruit cake and the Wallingford muffin, which can only be purchased at Annies. Teas include Assam, Ceylon, Darjeeling and Earl Grey.

Closed: Wednesdays throughout the year, also　Sundays in winter.

Belle Maison Gift Shop and Tearoom
43 St. Mary's Street
Wallingford
01491 825007

Disabled Access
Parking 100m.

Belle Maison Tearoom, a listed building,　is set in an old riverside market town, near to the castle gardens and boat station.　The table cloths are peach, with lace covers, and there are paper doilies under the cups. Pine chairs finish off the effect. Proprietor Alloray Crookston offers service, with courtesy and a smile as customers choose their tea. There is no set menu, but　Luxury Sandwiches and gateaux are reasonably priced and　home made. In season, a range of ice cream, sundaes and fresh fruit salads are available. Teas　include China and Earl Grey, and Colombian coffee is available.
A variety of gifts from floral arrangements and swags to toy rabbits and bears are available in the shop area.

Dingles Nook

45 Cartway
Bridgnorth
01746 767231

Parking 100m.

Situated on the banks of the River Severn by the old bridge, the listed building is not far from the cliff railway and Bishop Percy's House.

The house itself was built about 1650 and has a large inglenook fireplace and a host of old ships' timbers as beams and purlins. Proprietor Ann Bayliss prides herself on the cosy decor and warm, friendly service that greets customers as they enter the tea room.

A typical Tea offers a sandwich, a slice of cake or pie and a tea or coffee. Cakes and scones are all home made on the premises, and Ann has developed a reputation for the quality of her cooking over the years. Among the teas are Assam, Darjeeling and Earl Grey.

Northgate Pantry

Northgate
High Town
Bridgnorth
01746 767373

Parking 50m.

Next to the North Gate, the pantry is not far for visitors to take advantage of local places of interest such as the Severn Valley Railway and sights within the market town itself.

Cakes and scones are home baked and proprietor Lisa Edwards offers a good range of naughty sweets and old fashioned puds, including bread pudding, crumbles and fruit pies. The main teas available are Assam, Darjeeling and Earl Grey.

IRONBRIDGE

Painting Shop Tea Room
Maws Craft Centre
Jackfield
Ironbridge
Nr. Telford
01952 883843

Disabled Access
Parking on site

The Painting Shop Tea Room is part of the Maws Craft Centre in the heart of Ironbridge, and derives its name from being built as part of the tileworks in the 1830s. Inside, the original walls and floor tiles remain.

Tea comprises a scone with jam and cream and a pot of tea, or speciality gateaux and a cup of coffee. Cakes, scones and jams are all home made and house favourites include carrot cake, chocolate crunch, strawberry flapjack, treacle tart and apple pie. Newly-wed proprietors Russell and Nicky Gouldbourn have won a Heartbeat Award for serving healthy food. There is a good range of teas.

Closed: Mondays (except Bank Holidays).

LEINTWARDINE

Fiddlers Tea Room
10 Rosemary Lane
Leintwardine
Nr. Craven Arms
01547 540610

Disabled Access
Parking 50m.

The barn is about two hundred and fifty years old and has recently been sympathetically restored, making a feature of the original beams. One internal wall has been retained in local stone. Outside is a fully enclosed patio area. Cream Tea comprises two scones with jam and clotted cream, cake and tea or coffee. Cakes, scones and jams are all home made and there is a selection of freshly ground coffees served in cafetieres. Among the teas available are Assam, Ceylon, China, Darjeeling and Earl Grey.

Closed: Mondays, and from the end September to Easter.

The Malthouse Tearooms

44 High Street   Parking outside
Much Wenlock
01952 728419

The Malthouse Tearooms are within easy reach of the priory and local mediaeval buildings. Set in a 17th century malthouse, the tea rooms are on the first floor, with antiques for sale on the ground and second floors. The very low, beamed ceilings and chintz curtains give a traditional atmosphere, as do the uniformed waitresses.

Tea serves a round of ham and salad sandwiches, a scone with jam and cream, a slice of cake and a pot of tea per person. Alternatively, a round of sandwiches are accompanied by a toasted teacake, lemon meringue pie with fresh cream and a pot of tea. Cakes, scones, quiches and puddings are home baked daily, and proprietor Lynette Ashworth guarantees that nothing is ever frozen.

Closed: Tuesdays in winter season.

SIX ASHES

Six Ashes Tearooms and Restaurant

Six Ashes   Parking on site
Nr. Bridgnorth
01384 221216

The attractive Victorian style building has won praise from many quarters. Inside, low, beamed ceilings, stone walls and an open fire creates a relaxing atmosphere. Dozens of teapots and plates are displayed, along with dried flowers on the tables. Background music is unobtrusive and classical and there is waitress service. A large choice of home baked bread, scones and cakes, jams and cream are available in season for guests to compile the Tea of their choice. Among the teas in the pot are Assam, Ceylon, China, Darjeeling and Earl Grey.

Closed: Mondays, Tuesdays and Fridays in winter, Mondays and Tuesdays only in summer.

Hillside Cottage Tearooms
The Cliffs
Cheddar
01934 743158

Parking 100m.

Situated between Gough's and Cox's Caves on the opposite side of the road, overlooking a large picturesque lake, the tearooms are set in about a third of an acre of terraced gardens. The two hundred year old cottage was re-established as a tearoom in 1984, having been a tearoom around the turn of the century. Behind towers the massive bulk of Lion Rock.
Cream Tea serves two sultana scones, clotted cream and jam with a pot of tea for one. Cakes and scones are home baked, with apple pie, sultana flapjack, cherry shortcake and farmhouse fruitcake all tempting the hungry customer. There is also an extensive range of Childhay Manor real dairy ice cream sundaes. Teas include Assam, Darjeeling and Earl Grey.

CREWKERNE

Crumms
Unit 9
St George Centre
Crewkerne
01460 76965

Disabled Access
Parking on site

Opposite "Leos" supermarket in a pretty shopping arcade, Crumms is a Coffee/ Tea Shop. The small eatery is clean with reasonable prices and the option of eating al fresco, weather permitting. There is no set menu to give as wide a choice as possible, with cakes and scones all home made. Sandwiches are the main speciality, with healthy, fresh products used.
Among the range of teas are Assam, Darjeeling and Earl Grey as well as herbal varieties.

Closed: Sundays, Christmas period and all Bank Holidays.

The Tea Shoppe

3 High Street
Dunster
01643 821304

Disabled Access
Parking 50m.

The Tea Shoppe retains old elm beams, two original staircases and pil reed ceilings made from reeds grown in Dunster Marshes. Established as a tea room in the 1930s, its polished table tops, open fire and cottage decor, have made it a popular venue for visitors from all over the world.

Dunster Cream Tea offers two all-butter scones, thick clotted cream, strawberry jam and a pot of tea. Rustic breads, scones and cakes are all freshly baked in the kitchen's Aga, and proprietors, Norman and Pamela Goldsack ensure that all their dishes are as fresh as possible. Brown sugar meringues are popular, and teas include Assam, Ceylon, China, Darjeeling and Earl Grey. Lemonade is home made.

Closed: Thursdays, Weekdays from November to December, and all of January and February.

GLASTONBURY

Abbey Tea Rooms and Restaurant

16 Magdalene Street
Glastonbury
01458 832852

Disabled Access
Parking opposite

The building itself is five hundred years old, with pretty pink decor, crockery, tablecloths and fresh flowers. It is completely Non Smoking. In winter the cosy atmosphere is enhanced by a fire.

Somerset Cream Tea comprises two home made scones with local clotted cream and strawberry jam served with a pot of tea. Cakes and scones are home baked and attractively displayed for easy selection and locally made ice cream is also available. The emphasis is on healthy eating as proprietor Mary Parker has just won a Heartbeat Award. There is a good choice of over ten different teas, and local cider is on sale.

Closed: Sunday mornings during winter months.

GLASTONBURY

The Monarch Tearooms
15A High Street
Glastonbury
01458 835033

Disabled Access
Parking to rear

Not far from the Abbey and Tor, The Monarch Tearooms can be found up the alleyway between Adam's and the hand made shoe shop.
The interior dates from 1720, having been the old wine cellar of the Monarch public house. It has vaulted ceilings and is easy on the eye.
Cream Tea offers two home made scones with clotted cream, jam and a pot of tea for one. There is a range of home baked cakes and scones and sometimes home made jam. There are thirty teas available altogether.

HORNER

The Horner Tea Gardens
Horner
Nr. Porlock
01643 862380

Disabled Access
Parking 50m.

Situated on Exmoor and not far from Dunkery Beacon and Horner Water which offer walks and horse riding, the Horner Tea Gardens enjoys panoramic scenic views of the surrounding countryside.
The Grade II listed building welcomes dogs and can cater for parties. Parking is within fifty metres.
Cream Tea consists of tea, scones, clotted cream and jam. Cakes and scones are home baked and the local tea is blended to suit the area. Earl Grey is also available.

Closed: End of October to mid March.

PORLOCK   **Somerset**

Camellia Tea and Coffee House

High Street   Disabled Access
Porlock   Parking 50m.
01643 862266

Hand-stitched tapestries and the photographs which are for sale give a homely ambience to Cammellia Tea and Coffee House, as does the centrepiece, an antique Welsh dresser. The House is Non-Smoking throughout. Well-behaved dogs are welcome. Cream Tea serves two home made scones, clotted cream and jam with a pot of tea of the customer's choice. Cakes are home baked, and sandwiches with unusual fillings such as pears, blue cheese and walnuts, or chicken, avocado and apple chutney are a regular speciality. Earl Grey and a selection of fruit teas provide liquid refreshment.

Closed: Sunday mornings and Tuesdays, all of December and January, and weekdays in November and February.

TRISCOMBE

Stable Cottage Tea Rooms

Stable Cottage   Disabled Access
Triscombe   Parking on site
Nr. Taunton
01984 618239

Stable Cottage Tea Rooms are set in proprietor Susan Bucknall's own grounds, with magnificent views of the Quantock Hills. The building is part of a complete stable yard, including the original tack room. The unique setting boasts wood-pannelling and sporting pictures on the walls, is popular with locals and ideally placed for visitors.
Somerset Clotted Cream Tea offers two scones with jam, cream and a pot of tea. Farmhouse Tea serves a free range boiled or poached egg from Susan's hens on toast, a slice of cake and tea as the Farmhouse. Cakes and scones are baked on site and there is a good range of teas, including Assam, Ceylon, China, Darjeeling and Earl Grey.

Closed: Weekdays in Winter.

STAFFORD   **Staffordshire**

Cottage Tea Room
Market Street   Parking on site
Stafford
01785 716091

The tea room is located halfway up Market Street near to the busy market which takes place on Wednesdays and Saturdays. Inside, the tea room's friendly atmosphere is enhanced by the tasteful decor in cottage style. Tables and chairs are in antique oak.

Cream Tea serves a large scone with jam and fresh cream and a pot of tea. For those who prefer savouries, there is a ham sandwich with potato crisps and salad garnish, a slice of coffee and walnut cake and a pot of tea . Cakes and scones are home baked and there is a choice of sultana or cherry scone. The teas in the pot are Ceylon, Darjeeling and Earl Grey.

Closed: Sundays and Mondays.

TAMWORTH

Clarke's Tea Shoppe
7 King's Street   Disabled Access
Tamworth   Parking 50m.
01827 51400

Located on the small road between Church and Market Streets, Clarke's Tea Shoppe is close to the Saxon Castle, the church with a spiral staircase and the bowling alley. Market Days are Tuesdays and Saturdays.

Clarke's is a modern version of a tea shoppe. A Non-Smoking environment, it has a healthy eating menu. Cream Tea and cakes are homemade. The house specialities are the teabreads, and there is a good selection of teas, including Assam, Ceylon, China, Darjeeling and Earl Grey.

Closed: Sundays during winter season.

UPPER HULME

Roaches Tea Room

Paddock Farm
Upper Hulme
Nr. Leek
01538 300345

Disabled Access
Parking on site

Situated by the Roaches, overlooking Tittesworth Reservoir and Leek, the area is popular with walkers. It is also close to the small market town with factory shops and conveniently situated for Alton Towers.

Views from the tea room are magnificent, and inside, the oak beams and inglenook fireplace, which has a wood-burning stove, give a cosy atmosphere. A grandfather clock, Welsh dresser, oak corner cupboard and settle add to the homely ambience. In mild weather it is possible to sit outside.

Cream Tea serves up two scones with jam, fresh cream and a pot of tea, and scones and cakes are home baked. As well as a variety of cakes, lemon meringue, pavlova, apple pie and Cheshire Farm ice cream with no artificial ingredients, there is herbal tea and Earl Grey as refreshment.

-------0-------

Should I, after tea and cakes and ices,
Have the strength to force the moment to its crisis?

(T.S. Eliot - Portrait of a Lady)

Yesteryear's Tea Shoppe

17 Church Street
Clare
Nr. Sudbury
01787 278809

Parking 50m.

Yesteryear's Tea Shoppe is situated opposite Suffolk Sale Rooms and behind the church. It is not far from Clare Country Park and Priory. Visitors enjoy the open fireplace in winter and the oak-beamed interior, while enjoying tea from Willow Pattern tableware at a lace covered table.

Cream Teas offer two scones with jam, cream and a pot of tea or coffee. The Morning or Afternoon Special includes an assortment of freshly prepared sandwiches, scones, cakes and tea or coffee.

Cakes, scones and jams are home made, the cups of coffee are bottomless and there is a good selection of teas, amongst them, Assam, Ceylon, China, Darjeeling and Earl Grey.

FELIXSTOWE

The Corner House

47 Undercliffe Road West
Felixstowe
01394 283939

Disabled Access
Parking 50m.

The Corner House is set opposite the Leisure Centre and is local to the port, ferry, Languard Fort and the beach.

The interior is well-decorated with various items of interest on the walls. There is no set menu. Cakes and scones are home baked and priced separately to allow for a greater choice. Among the teas are Assam, and Earl Grey.

Closed: Mondays (except Bank Holidays).

FELIXSTOWE

Suffolk

Oaks Tea Room

1 Crescent Road
Felixstowe
01394 273444

Disabled Access
Parking opposite

Right in the centre of town known as "The Triangle" and opposite the cinema. Oaks Tea Room is ideal for walks in Constable country and the Nature Reserve, and is handy for the Fort-Foot Ferry to Bawdsey Island. Inside is a relaxing atmosphere where traditional values and service are foremost.

The Afternoon Special offers an assortment of sandwiches with a scone, a selection of cakes and pastries and a pot of tea. Cream Tea comprises two warmed scones, thick double cream, strawberry jam and a pot of tea. Bread, cakes and scones are all home baked and there is a wide range of house specials including the cherry flapjack, apricot and coconut slice, various flavours of scone and butter and freshly squeezed orange juice. Among the teas are Darjeeling and Earl Grey.

LAVENHAM

Tickle Manor

17 High Street
Lavenham
Nr. Sudbury
01787 248438

Parking 50m.

Situated in the High Street in historic Lavenham, the tea room was built in 1530 and the original beams are now exposed to give an authentically historic feel. Portmeirion china is used throughout, adding to the atmosphere.

All cakes, puddings and scones are home made. Ham and Jersey cream are supplied locally, bread and rolls by the baker. Only Twinings teas are used, including Assam, Ceylon, Darjeeling and Earl Grey, and a selection of herbal teas, natural fruit juices and elderflower and citrus presse.

COMPTON   **Surrey**

The Tea Shop
Down Lane   Disabled Access
Compton   Parking outside
Nr. Guildford
01483 811030

The Tea Shop building is almost a hundred years old and the decor is random
as regular customers like it that way. Sally and Timothy Porter are a mother
and son partnership who have been in the Egon Ronay Guide since 1987.
Cream Tea comprises tea or coffee with a scone, jam, cream and a slice of
cake. Otherwise there is no set menu. Cakes, scones and jams are home made
along with Jersey cream and free range eggs. There is an extensive range of
soft drinks, including exotic seltzers and aqua libra and a vast selection of
fifty teas.

DORKING

Hasketts Tea and Coffee Shop
86B South Street   Disabled Access
Dorking   Parking 100m.
01306 885833

Set in the beautiful surrounding countryside and the unique atmosphere of
Dorking, which was first mentioned in the Domesday Book, the tea room is
housed in a Grade Two listed building, dating back to 1680. Decor is based
faithfully on 1920-35 and has been widely acclaimed for its style and quality
of presentation. Low drop pink or blue tablecloths are topped with traditional
Nottingham lace.
Cream Tea is two scones, strawberry or raspberry seedless jam with whipped
cream and a choice of tea. Cakes, scones and jams are all home made and
there is a choice of a minimum of twenty cakes always available. There is a
selection of eighteen teas or for those who prefer coffee, there is a choice of a
dozen, all served in cafetieres.

GUILDFORD

Surrey

Guildford House Tea Room

155 High Street
Guildford
01483 454608

Parking 100m.

Guildford House Tea Room dates from about 1660. The tea room is on the lower ground level with traditional dark furniture, terracotta coloured tablecloths and white china. Weather permitting, a large courtyard with garden chairs is suitable for eating out of doors.

Cream Tea comprises a pot of tea per person, two large scones, strawberry jam and whipped double cream. Cakes and jams are home made and the favourites are carrot cake with lemon topping, farmhouse fruit cake and brown sugar and walnut tart, served with double cream. To wash it all down there is a choice of tea, including Assam, Darjeeling and Earl Grey.

Closed: Sundays and Mondays.

RANMORE

The Old Cartlodge Tearooms

Dunley Hill Farm
Ranmore Common
Nr. Dorking
01483 282222

Disabled Access
Parking on site

Ideal for walkers on the North Downs' Way and close to Denbies' Wine Estate, The Old Cartlodge Tearooms are housed in a converted farm building on a working farm, set off the road. Ninety per cent of the room is Non-Smoking. Tables and chairs are in pine and the building is full of rustic charm.

Cream Tea consists of two scones, cream, jam and butter. Cakes and scones are home made and proprietor Mary Suckling makes a feature of her cakes, which can be taken home for the rest of the family to enjoy as well. Herb teas join the regulars Assam, Darjeeling and Earl Grey.

Closed: Mondays, and from 21st December to beginning of February.

BEXHILL-ON-SEA

Seashells Tea Rooms
54 Western Road
Bexhill-on-Sea
01424 730019

Disabled Access
Parking outside

Two doors away from the library, Seashells Tea Rooms offer a selection of items for visitors. Bread, cakes, scones and jams come from the bakery and in warm weather guests enjoy sitting in the tea garden.

Closed: Sundays.

BODIAM

Knollys
The Main Street
Bodiam
01580 830323

Disabled Access
Parking on site

The tea room and garden adjoin and have direct access to the castle and grounds of Bodiam Castle, opposite the village green.
Cream Tea serves a pot of tea with two scones, strawberry jam and cream. High Tea offers salmon and cucumber or prawn salad sandwiches with home made, fresh cream cake and a pot of tea.
Cakes and scones are home baked, and specialities to tempt the palate include pavlova, passion cake, apricot pie and chocolate cake. Local strawberries are also available in season. Among the teas are Assam, Darjeeling, Earl Grey and Lapsang.

Closed: Mondays (except Bank Holidays) and October to Easter.

DITCHLING   **East Sussex**

Mansfield
17-19 High Street
Ditchling   Parking 100m.
01273 844033

Halfway up the High Street, Mansfield is near to Ditchling Museum, the
wildlife park and various walks. The Grade II listed building is about 350
years old. Half timber-framed, with Victorian frontage its interior still boasts
ancient beams. Food is served on Wedgewood bone china inside and white
bone china outside in the country style tea garden.
There is no set tea menu, but an assortment of home made cakes and scones
including Victoria sponges, teacakes and fruit pies can be combined to make
a satisfying break. Among the teas are Assam, Darjeeling, Earl Grey, English
Breakfast, Lapsang Souchong, Rose Pouchong and various herbal infusions.

Closed: Mondays to Fridays.

EASTBOURNE

Dickens Tea Cottage
5 South Street
Eastbourne   Parking 50m.
01323 732637

Established in 1946, Dickens Tea Cottage is managed by Penelope and George
Kyprianou and is located in an attractive eighteenth century building close to
the town centre, sea and theatres. Oak beams, prints and, in winter, an open
fire, create a relaxing atmosphere which is complemented by fine china and a
friendly waitress service. It is easy to believe that Charles Dickens once visited.
Special Sussex Cream Teas or Tea and Cake make a reasonably priced treat
and there is a choice of China and Earl Grey tea. Scones, cakes and pies are
baked on the premises, with an accent on old fashioned cakes such as Melting
Moments.

Closed: Sundays and Mondays.

The Pavilion Tea Rooms
Royal Parade   Parking 50m.
Eastbourne
01323 410374

The traditional Victorian/Edwardian tea room is situated on the sea front, with a gift shop and sun lounge on site and waitress service.

A member of the Tea Council and Guild of Tea Shops, special attractions which make this venue unique include golf and croquet on the lawns and a pianist to play every afternoon and evening in summer.

Sussex Cream Tea serves buttered sultana scones with whipped cream, strawberry preserve and a pot of pavilion tea for one. There is a large selection of biscuits, patisserie, ice cream sundaes and sorbets. Among the teas are Assam, Ceylon, China, Darjeeling and Earl Grey.

EAST HOATHLY

Clara's
9 High Street   Parking adjacent
East Hoathly
Nr. Lewes
01825 840339

Clara's is situated in the middle of a quiet bypassed village close to the church, Thomas Turner's house and the pottery. Oak beams are testimony to the fact that the building dates from about 1760. It is one of the three tea rooms in Sussex in the Guild of Tea Shops set up by the Tea Council.

Cakes, scones and jam are home made and Cream Tea comprises a pot of tea for one, two scones, butter, jam and cream. Clara's Special offers a pot of tea, toasted, buttered teacake with cream and jam. The main teas are Darjeeling and Earl Grey. As well as food, Clara's sells local honey, jams and chutneys, a wide range of gifts, cards, bric-a-brac and Rowan knitting yarns.

Closed: Mondays and Tuesdays, and from Christmas to mid-January.

Bentley Tearooms

Bentley Wildfowl and Motor Museum
Halland
Nr. Uckfield
01825 840344

Disabled Access
Parking 100m.

Located inside the Bentley Wildfowl Park with signposts off the main roads, Bentley Tearooms is situated at the entrance to the hundred acre park with the historic Motor Museum and Manor House and overlooks fields and the steam model railway.

Visitors can gorge on Cream Teas with Devon clotted cream and genuinely home baked cakes, pies and scones are prepared on the premises. There is a choice of Darjeeling or Earl Grey and a full range of herbal teas.

Closed: November to January, and February to Easter, weekends only.

HOVE

Pavilion Tea House

Hove Park
Park View Road
Hove
01273 727003

Disabled Access
Parking 50m.

Housed in the old style cricket pavilion, with panoramic views of the park, there is seating inside the Pavilion and on the verandah which overlooks the tennis courts and bowling greens. The large tea garden is surrounded by beautifully well-kept flower beds and an arbour.

Locally baked cakes and pastries are available along with a large selection of sandwiches, ice creams, soft drinks and confectionery. In cold weather, warming soup can be ordered as well as a choice of Assam, Ceylon or Earl Grey Tea, coffee or hot chocolate.

Closed: November to February inclusive.

Coach House Tearoom
Old London Road   Disabled Access
Patcham   Parking 50m.
Nr. Brighton
01273 553243

Set in the village street next door to the bakery, owned by proprietors Brian
and Rae Berrystone, the Coach House Tearoom is near to the longest tythe
barn in Sussex. The traditional coach house has high wooden entrance doors,
flint walls and a gallery and a wonderful atmosphere. The walled patio has a
small pond with fountain.
Cream Tea comprises two large scones with butter, cream, jam and a pot of
tea. Bread, cakes, scones and jams are all made on site featuring mouthwatering
specialities such as apricot and chocolate meringue and hot cherries with cream
and Italian ice cream. Among the teas are Assam, Ceylon, China, Darjeeling
and Earl Grey.

Closed: Mondays all year, and Sundays during the winter season.

PEASMARSH

Pond Cottage Tea Rooms
Jempson and Bailey Ltd.   Disabled Access
Main Street   Parking on site
Peasmarsh
Nr. Rye
01797 230214

Pond Cottage Tea Rooms are housed in a Grade II listed building, dating about
1600, and restored in 1993. The old wooden beams and open fireplace give a
traditional feel. Outside are gardens in the countryside, with additional seating
and a play area for the children.
Sussex Cream Teas offer two fruit scones with real Cornish clotted cream,
jam and a pot of tea or cup of coffee, or there is a slice of gateaux with a pot of
tea or cup of coffee. All bread, cakes, scones and jams are home made in the
traditional bakehouse. Teas include Assam, Ceylon, China, Darjeeling and
Earl Grey.

Fletcher's House

2 Lion Street
Rye
01797 223101

Disabled Access
Parking 100m.

The Tudor building dates from 1430 and was the birth place of dramatist, John Fletcher. Inside all food is served on Wedgewood tableware.
The Classic Country Cream Tea consists of a choice of tea, with home baked scone, whipped cream from a local farm, strawberry or bramble jam and a dainty cream cheese and cucumber sandwich. All cakes are baked in the kitchen on site, using only high quality ingredients. A taste of the house speciality cakes are chocolate fudge, Battenburg, creamy cheesecake and rich Scottish ginger. There is a good selection of teas including Assam, Ceylon, China, Darjeeling and Earl Grey. After such refreshment, guests may well want to browse through the gift shop on site.

Grist Mill Tearoom

The Grist Mill
The Strand
Rye
01797 225784

Disabled Access
Parking on site

The historic stone building was built in about 1746 to store the entire provisions for Rye. Later on it was used as a corn grinding mill. There is a spacious seating area, whilst large balcony doors on the first floor provide a bright and airy atmosphere in summer.
Sussex Cream Teas consist of two very large scones with local unpasteurised dairy cream, jam, butter and a pot of tea. All food is served on Victorian style china, with a wide selection of teas and exceptional coffee. Bread, cakes and scones are all home baked and as well as herbal and fruit teas, Assam, Ceylon, Darjeeling and Earl Grey feature.

Swan Cottage Tearooms

41 The Mint Disabled Access
Rye Parking 100m.
01797 222423

This fifteenth century former inn has two rooms for its guests. The front room for smokers and a large rear room with inglenook fireplace, for Non Smokers. Tastefully decorated with wooden tables and chairs Swan Cottage also uses interesting table mats with scenes of Surrey and all white Sussex tableware from Villeroy and Boch.

Swan Cottage Afternoon Tea serves a pot of tea, with a choice of sandwich, two home made fruit scones, butter jam and fresh cream. Sussex Cream Tea offers a pot of tea with two scones, butter, jam and fresh cream. Cakes and scones are home baked with a large selection of fresh cream gateaux, cakes and pastries, including chocolate cream gateau and lemon drizzle cake. There is a choice of Ceylon or Earl Grey tea.

Closed: Tuesdays, and mid-October to mid-May.

-------0-------

Tea does our fancy aid,
Repress those vapours which the head invade
and keeps the palace of the soul serene
Fit on her birthday to salute the Queen.

(Edmund Waller)

BALCOMBE

The Balcombe Tea Rooms
Bramble Hill
Balcombe
01444 811777

Disabled Access
Parking on site

Set in the village centre in a popular walking area close to the viaduct, High Beech Gardens, Nymans Gardens and Borde Hill Gardens, The Balcombe Tea Rooms are set in a designated area of outstanding beauty.

Clotted Cream Tea presents a pot of tea, two home made scones, jam and clotted cream. Cakes and scones are home baked, and the tea rooms specialise in old fashioned bread pudding, fresh cream cakes and raspberries and strawberries in season. Among the teas are Assam, Darjeeling, Earl Grey and Lapsang.

Closed: Mondays (except Bank Holidays), and Christmas to mid-January.

BOGNOR REGIS

The Lantern Tea Rooms
78 Aldwick Road
Bognor Regis
01243 821537

Disabled Access
Parking 50m.

Opposite the pine showroom and three hundred yards from the beach and putting green, The Lantern Tea Rooms are in a listed building.

Cream Teas offer two scones wth jam, cream and a pot of tea. Cakes and scones are home baked and there is a choice of Assam and Earl Grey tea.

Closed: Sundays.

St. Martin's Tea Rooms
3 St. Martin's Street
Chichester
01243 786715

Parking 50m.

St. Martin's Tea Rooms are set in the middle of an historic city. The large double-fronted Mediaeval building with Georgian frontage has been carefully restored, and Keith Nelson, the proprietor, has spent the last twenty years personally preserving the character of the building. He has also ensured that food and drink is of the highest quality, with healthy eating a priority. Organic bread, cakes and scones are all home baked and all ingredients are written out for the items, which include carrot yoghurt cake, nutty fruit flapjack and banana bread.

The wide range of teas includes among its number Assam, Ceylon, China, Darjeeling, Earl Grey and many more.

Closed: Sundays.

FINDON

Old Forge Tea Rooms
Nepcote Lane
Findon
01903 877431

Disabled Access
Parking 50m.

The Old Forge Tea Rooms are situated on the road from the village square to Cissbury Ring, an Iron-Age hill fort and Chanctonbury Ring.

Tradition, good quality, style and presentation is the tea rooms' motto, and this is borne out in the immaculately pinnied and mob-capped waitress service, lace tablecloths and attention to detail such as cubed sugar and tongs, or butter curls.

Cream Tea serves a scone, butter, jam, thick cream and a pot of tea. Findon Tea provides a selection of delicious finger sandwiches, the cream tea, cakes and a pot of tea. Cakes, scones and jams are home made, with a choice of eight types of scone. Loose leaf teas include Lapsang and Jasmine, Imperial Spiced and favourites like Assam, Ceylon, China, Darjeeling and Earl Grey.

Norton House Tearooms

High Street
Henfield
01273 492064

Disabled Access
Parking 50m.

Located near the home of the Sussex Wildlife Trust, Norton House Tearooms are ideal for enthusiastic walkers taking a break. The timbered house with Queen Anne facade was restored in 1968/9 by its present owners. It is furnished with traditional oak tables and chairs, which complement the old brick fireplaces and wooden beams and there is a delightful old English garden for summer weather.

Cream Tea comprises two scones with butter, jam, cream and tea. Bread, cakes, scones and jams are home made, with Norton House rock cakes a speciality. To wash it down there is Lyons Quick Brew or a choice of Assam, China, Darjeeling, Earl Grey, Keemun or Lapsang.

Closed: Tuesdays all year; Wednesdays also from Christmas to Easter.

KIRDFORD

Russets Tea Room

Kirdford Growers Ltd.
Kirdford
Nr. Billingshurst
01403 820003

Disabled Access
Parking on site

Russets Tea Room is part of Kirdford Growers, a practising apple farm, established around a hundred years ago and renowned for its selection of apple juices and ciders. The tea room has classic country style decor inside, along with a children's play area and a craft shop.

Cream Tea furnishes one person with two scones, fresh cream, jam, butter and a cup of tea for one or two people. Set tea comprises a round of sandwiches, slice of cake and cream tea as above. Cakes and scones are home baked and there is a wide choice of teas. Kirdford apple juice features for those who prefer a cold drink.

Closed: Mondays and Tuesdays all year.

MIDHURST

Ye Olde Tea Shoppe
North Street
Midhurst
01730 813481

Disabled Access
Parking 100m.

Set in the lower part of the main street, Ye Olde Tea Shoppe is not far from Cowdray Park, where polo is played, and Cowdray Castle. The Grade II listed building dates back to 1545, with a wealth of old beams. Jackie and Ian Dummer, the proprietors, have also uncovered a sixteenth century wall painting which is awaiting restoration. H.G. Wells reputedly stayed in one of the bedrooms.

Cream Tea provides two scones with jam, double cream and tea for one. Or there is teacake and tea or two crumpets and tea. Cakes, scones and jams are all home baked and specialities include treacle tart, passion cake and chocolate fudge cake. Among the teas are Assam, China, Darjeeling and Earl Grey.

PETWORTH

Tudor Cottage Cafe
Sadlers Row
Petworth
01798 342125

Disabled Access
Parking 50m.

Situated at the entrance to the town car park, Tudor Cottage Cafe is not far from Petworth House, a National Trust property, and Petworth Park, which was created by Capability Brown. The Tudor Cottage was built in 1475 and boasts wooden beams as part of the low ceilings, and a log fire in the original fireplaces in winter.

Cream Teas and Crumpet Tea fill the hungry visitor. Cakes, scones and jams are home made and among the teas are Assam, Ceylon, China, Darjeeling and Earl Grey.

SOUTH FERRING   West Sussex

The Pantry
1A The Pantiles   Disabled Access
Ferringham Lane
South Ferring
01903 503957

The tearoom provides a setting for Sussex crafts and paintings. Although only small, it is cosy, with old fashioned gate-leg tables complementing the traditional style of the tearoom. The various sizes and colours of the china teapots often provoke favourable comment.

Cream Tea comprises a pot of tea with two home made scones, butter, jam and clotted cream. Cakes, biscuits, jams and marmalades are also home made, and specialities include fresh cream meringues. Indian and herbal teas are available, along with Earl Grey.

Closed: Wednesdays all day, and Sunday mornings.

WALBERTON

"Beam Ends"
Hedgers Hill   Parking on site
Walberton
Nr. Arundel
01243 551254

Close to Arundel, Climping Beach and Binsted Woods, "Beam Ends" is a good place to stop for a rest. The 16th century thatched cottage is set in one acre of wooded garden, with fine views over the valley. Inside, the thirties style tea room indulges its visitors with linen tablecloths, fresh flowers, old fashioned crockery and an open fire.

Cream Tea comprises two home made scones with butter, jam, whipped cream and a pot of tea. The "Beam Ends" Special serves a round of sandwiches with cream tea, as above, and home made cake. Cakes, scones and jams are home made and the selection of teas includes Natural Fruit Tea, Assam, Ceylon, China, Darjeeling and Earl Grey.

Closed: Mondays (except Bank Holidays), all of January.

The Copper Kettle Cafe
1 John Street   Disabled Access
Cullercoats   Parking 50m.
0191 251 3616

A few steps away from the seafront overlooking Cullercoats Bay, with views of Tynemouth Castle and Priory, The Copper Kettle Cafe is just the place after a visit to the beach.

There is no set menu, but a large range of sandwiches, made with home baked bread and home made cakes, scones and fruit tarts demand attention. There is a good choice of soft drinks such as milk shakes and fresh fruit juices or a selection of fruit and herbal teas alongside the favourites Assam, Ceylon, China, Darjeeling and Earl Grey.

Closed: Mondays in summer; Mondays to Wednesdays in winter.

JESMOND

"Acorns"
15 Acorn Road   Parking 50m.
Jesmond
Nr. Newcastle-upon Tyne
0191 281 1862

The cosy, Non-Smoking tea and coffee room is adjacent to Brown's Contemporary Art Gallery. It is personally supervised by proprietors Robert and Sheila Nicholson, with the able assistance of personable part-time staff currently studying at Newcastle University.

A choice of sandwich, scone or toasted teacake with strawberry preserve comes with a pot of tea, or can include a choice of patisserie. Cakes and scones are home baked. The home made banoffi pie is a favourite, as is the cointreau and orange cheesecake. Favourite thirst quenchers are Assam, Darjeeling and Earl Grey teas.

Closed: Sundays.

NORTH SHIELDS

Tyne and Wear

The Olde Anchor Tea Shop
6 Ferry Mews
New Quay
North Shields
0191 257 6537

Disabled Access
Parking on site

Enjoying a riverside position in the old ferry building, with the Art Gallery and Nauticalia Shop next door, The Olde Anchor Tea Shop has a nautical theme running through it, with ships' crests, photographs and paintings and anchors on display.

There is no set menu as proprietor Michael Davis likes to offer his customers as much variety as possible. Cakes, scones, pies, biscuits and confectionery are all home made and there is a good range of teas available, including Ceylon, China, Darjeeling and Earl Grey.

WHITLEY BAY

The Tearooms
4 Marden Road
Whitley Bay
0191 252 3943

Disabled Access
Parking 50m.

This Non-Smoking establishment has been run by Alma and Sidney Heppell since 1987 and is situated opposite St. Paul's Church, near to the Sealife Centre in Marden Quarry. Inside, there are two large, well-decorated rooms. The tablecloths are pink and complement the bone china tableware. In summer it is possible to sit on the patio. The carpets add cosiness and warmth to the venue in winter.

There is no set menu, but sandwiches, tea and cakes all feature on a reasonably priced menu. Specialities in winter are the sweet mince pies with cream. Fresh fruit flans celebrate the warmer season, meringues are a perennial favourite and the fruit and cheese scones are baked daily along with the other produce. Teas include Assam, Ceylon, China, Darjeeling and Earl Grey.

Closed: Sundays, Mondays and Wednesdays.

ALCESTER

Present Shoppe and Alcester Coffee House

12 High Street
Alcester
01789 765126

Disabled Access
Parking 50m.

Set in the middle of the High Street, the Present Shoppe and Alcester Coffee House are found in a Grade II listed building dating from 1642, which makes it the oldest shop in the High Street. Lace tablecloths and bone china add to the historical feel. Cream Teas furnish the rumbling tummy with a scone, strawberry jam and clotted cream and a cake from the display or two scones with cream and strawberry jam. Scones and cakes are home baked and clotted cream is delivered each week from Cornwall. Specialities include hot fruit flan with clotted cream and chocolate sponge pudding with chocolate sauce and ice cream. Among the teas are China, Darjeeling and Earl Grey.

Closed: Tuesdays.

DUNCHURCH

Crumb's Tea Rooms

3 Southam Road
Dunchurch
Nr. Rugby
01788 522489

Parking 50m.

Crumb's Tea Rooms overlook the hustle and bustle of the ancient village with its thatched cottages and stocks on the green. Tastefully furnished and prettily decorated it is a perfect retreat for light refreshment. The friendly atmosphere and waitress service give a traditional atmosphere along with the china crockery, and collection of teapots.
Cream Teas offer a choice of freshly made sandwich and a cream tea for two or large toasted teacakes. Cakes and scones are all home baked and the clotted cream is brought from Cornwall. Fresh coffee and tea wash it all down with a choice of P.G. Tips, Camomile, Darjeeling and Earl Grey.

Closed: Mondays.

KENILWORTH

Warwickshire

Time for Tea
40 Castle Hill
Kenilworth
01926 512675

Disabled Access
Parking 50m.

The Grade II listed building has cheerful decor with pine tables and overlooks the "Little Virginia" hamlet of thatched cottages built at the time of Queen Elizabeth I's visit to the castle in 1575. There is a conservatory to the rear in which to take tea.

There is no set menu, but cakes and scones are home baked with a mouthwatering selection that makes it hard to choose from, including chocolate and orange cake, ginger, fig and walnut cake or coconut and honey. There is a good choice of teas such as Assam, Earl Grey, Jasmine and Lapsang Souchong.

Closed: Mondays.

STRATFORD-UPON-AVON

Bensons of Stratford-upon-Avon
4 Bard's Walk
Stratford-upon-Avon
01789 261116

Disabled Access
Parking 100m.

Two minutes from Shakespeare's birthplace and not far from Mary Arden's House and Ann Hathaways cottage, Bensons epitomises the atmosphere and tradition of English culture, with friendly staff dressed in pinstripe uniforms. Fine bone china and silver tableware, fresh flowers, menus reproduced onto a 1936 copy of the Daily Telegraph enhance this gracious establishment. Newspapers and magazines are available for those who wish to read.

Smoked salmon sandwiches with lemon and ground pepper, a freshly baked scone with cream and jam and a choice of speciality tea. Bread, cakes, scones and jam are all home made and there is an outstanding patisserie. Among the teas available are Assam, Ceylon, China, Darjeeling and Earl Grey.

Closed: Sundays in winter season.

CORSHAM

Wiltshire

Audrey's
55A High Street
Corsham
01249 714931

Disabled Access
Parking 100m.

Opposite the Royal Oak public house and near to the Town Hall, Audrey Brown's tea room provides all-round service, with a homely atmosphere and friendly approach to her customers which includes minding their shopping and passing on messages when necessary. Children are catered for, handicapped people very welcome and cleanliness is so much a way of life that guests are free to inspect the kitchen.

Cream Tea provides a basket of warm scones - as many as the customer can eat, along with butter, strawberry jam, cream and a pot of tea or coffee. Two toasted teacakes are accompanied by a pot of tea or coffee. Bread, cakes, scones and jams are all home made with traditional English food a speciality. Teas feature Assam, Ceylon, China, Darjeeling and Earl Grey. Any tips are sent away to charities involved with feeding the third world.

Closed: Sundays between October and Easter.

DYRHAM PARK

Tollgate Teashop
Oldfield Gatehouse
Dyrham Park
Nr. Chippenham
01225 891585

Disabled Access
Parking on site

The building was a tollhouse to Dyrham Park House which is now with the National Trust. It has panoramic views over the Welsh hills.

Cream Tea provides two large scones with strawberry jam, and clotted cream and all fare is home baked, with a selection of cakes. Teas available are China, Darjeeling and Earl Grey.

Closed: Mondays; two weeks over Christmas period.

MARLBOROUGH

Wiltshire

Polly Tea Rooms
The High Street
Marlborough
01672 512146

Disabled Access
Parking outside

Established around the time of World War Two, the Polly Tea Rooms and shop provide a range of confectionary, much of it home made. Coach parties are catered for and there is a Non-Smoking area. It is Egon Ronay recommended. Dark wooden beams, pink walls and floral tablecloths contribute to a traditional atmosphere.

A minimum charge allows a Polly Tea which comprises three large plain or muesli scones with jam and cream, or, for a bit extra, clotted cream. Gateaux Tea for the same price offers a slice of one of the gateaux, such as pistachio or walnut. There is also a range of smaller cakes and biscuits and speciality ice cream.

WESTBURY

"Cottage Teas"
16 Maristow Street
Westbury
01373 826418

Disabled Access
Parking 50m.

With a pink washed front and window boxes, "Cottage Teas" is close to the Victorian swimming pool and the pottery in old Westbury. In summer the tea garden is open, whilst in winter, there is a log fire in the large open fireplace. Exposed wooden beams give an olde worlde effect, as do the matching tablecloths and curtains.

Proprietor Jill Bailey employs traditional methods and ingredients when creating old fashioned goodies. A clotted cream tea, salmon sandwiches, a pot of tea for one and a toasted teacake comprises a reasonably priced tea. Other mouthwatering items on the menu include special syrup tart, lemon drizzle cake and home baked rice pudding. Among the teas are Assam, Ceylon, China, Darjeeling and Earl Grey.

Closed: Mondays and Sundays.

BAILDON

Yorkshire

The Westgate Teashop
Westgate House
9 Westgate
Baildon
Nr. Shipley
01274 53190

Parking 100m.

Close to Baildon Moors and Baildon Craft Centre, The Westgate Teashop is in the heart of Emmerdale country. It dates back to the 1850s when the adjoining building was the Mill and the teashop was the mill owner's home. Since then it has been a private school for young ladies, and a post office and bakery during World War Two. The Jowett family has owned the premises for over 33 years and David, the proprietor, is happy to welcome guests to Afternoon Tea. This comprises a choice of sandwiches, a scone with butter or fresh cream and tea. Bread, cakes and scones are baked on the premises and the main speciality tea on offer is Earl Grey.

Closed: Weekends in winter.

DANBY
The Moors Tea Rooms
The Moors Centre
Danby
01287 660362

Disabled Access
Parking on site

With wonderful views over the moors and dales, the Moors Tea Rooms are set in the Moors Centre for the National Park. The building is the former shooting lodge of the Danby estate and stands in beautiful grounds on the banks of the River Esk.
Completely refurbished for 1995 by local craftsmen, the tea rooms offer a warm welcome to the Park. Bread, cakes, scones and jams are all home baked, with specialities including Bakewell tart, treacle sponge, strawberries and cream and various ice creams. Among the teas are Assam, Darjeeling and Earl Grey.

Closed: Weekends between November and March.

Woods Tea Rooms

3A Wood Street
Doncaster
01302 327126

Disabled Access
Parking 50m.

Woods Tea Rooms enjoys luxurious decor, with fine china presenting the food. Full Afternoon Tea comprises sandwiches, scones with jam and cream and cake. Cakes and scones are all home baked and the scones are square! Another speciality is the apple strudel. Teas and coffees are by Taylors of Harrogate and the choice includes Assam, Ceylon, Darjeeling and Earl Grey.

Closed: Sundays and Bank Holidays.

EASINGWOLD

Clark's Tearooms

Windross Square
Market Place
Easingwold
01347 823143

Disabled Access
Parking 50m.

Set on the edge of Herriot country close to the Cotswolds and the Yorkshire Moors, Clark's Tearooms overlook the green from their position in the market place.

Members of the Guild of Tea Shops, proprietors Gerald and Judy Clark have provided a separate parlour for smokers and there are pavement tables when the weather permits. Afternoon Tea consists of a sandwich, a savoury such as a cornish pasty or sausage roll, two cakes, a scone with butter and jam and a pot of tea. Bread, cakes, scones and jam are all cooked in the bakery on the premises, and specialities to look out for include Yorkshire fruitcake with cheese and the toasted tealoaf which goes very well with the Yorkshire curd. Teas available include Ceylon, China, Darjeeling and Earl Grey.

Closed: Sundays.

Gatsby's Tea Rooms
1A Old Market (First Floor)   Parking 50m.
Halifax
01422 323905

Located opposite the central library and close to the open air market and Eureka, the children's museum, Gatsby's Tea Rooms are ideally situated in Halifax town centre. The Old Market was originally built to sell locally made cloth, but now houses various craft shops.

The tea room itself is spacious with tasteful tableware. There are various tea menus available, including assorted sandwiches, home made scones served with preserve and fresh cream, home made cakes and tea. Little Gatsby Afternoon Tea is for the children, offering a sandwich, fizzy drink and scone with preserve and fresh cream or a small cake. Among the teas are Assam, Darjeeling and Earl Grey.

Closed: Sundays.

HAWORTH

Heather Cottage Tea Rooms
25-27 Main Street   Disabled Access
Haworth   Parking 100m.
01535 644511

To be found at the lower end of the cobble Main Street, Heather Cottage Tea Rooms is near to the Bronte Museum, Worth Valley Railway and the Pennine Way. The building started as two weavers' cottages, built 270 years ago. Today the flagged floors, stone walls and original wood burning stove are novelty features like the lace tablecloths. Food is served on Indian Tree pottery.

A scone with jam, cream and tea comprises Cream Tea, and there are many individually priced items of home made fayre to tempt the palate, a few of which are cherry and almond cake, Yorkshire parkin, and shortbread. The teas include Assam, Darjeeling and Earl Grey.

Closed: Weekdays in November.

HEBDEN BRIDGE

Watergate Tearooms and Tea Garden

9 Bridge Gate
Hebden Bridge
Halifax

01422 842978

Disabled Access
Parking 50m.

Within easy reach of canal trips, museums and good walks, Watergate Tearooms and Tea Garden boasts original Winnie the Pooh pictures and an antique Austrian pine dresser. In the background 1920s Al Bowlly type music recaptures a period feel.

Scones and cakes are home baked and the teas on offer include China, Darjeeling and Earl Grey.

Closed: Fridays.

HOLMFIRTH

The Wrinkled Stocking Tea Room

30 Huddersfield Road
Holmfirth

01484 681408

Disabled Access
Parking 100m.

This is The Wrinkled Stocking Tea Room seen in the T.V. series "The Last of the Summer Wine" and is often frequented by the cast of the programme. Holmfirth Cream Tea offers a pot of tea or coffee with a scone, jam and cream. Afternoon Tea serves a choice of freshly made sandwich, a pot of tea or coffee and a choice of sweet. Cakes and scones are all home baked, though not by Nora Batty's fair hand, and teas include Ceylon, Darjeeling and Earl Grey.

Rascals Tea Shop

29 Waterside
Knaresborough
01423 863606

Disabled Access
Parking 50m.

Down the steps from the Castle and within easy reach of Mother Shipton's Cave, Rascals Tea Shop is by the waterside and boating, with butterflies decorating the outside walls. It has splendid views of the famous Knaresborough railway bridge.

Yorkshire Cream Tea furnishes tired sightseers with a sultana scone, whipped cream, strawberry jam and malt loaf with a pot of tea. Bread, cakes and scones are home baked, with cakes and pastries baked on the premises. Specialities include Yorkshire Fat Rascals and Yorkshire Curd Tarts. There is a children's menu and a choice of Darjeeling and Earl Grey teas.

Closed: Weekdays, November to March.

LEEDS

Canal Gardens Victoria Tearooms

Princess Avenue
Leeds
01132 370495

Parking 100m.

Attached to Tropical World, reputedly the second most visited place in England, the tea room is near to the jungle walk and butterfly house.

Waitress service brings visitors their afternoon tea.

This is well-priced, with a toasted crumpet or muffin, a scone with jam and cream, fruit cake and cheese and fresh cream meringue. Cakes and scones are home made and the selection of teas include Assam, Ceylon, China, Darjeeling and Earl Grey.

Temple Newsam Tea Room

Temple Newsam Park   Parking 100m.
Leeds
01132 602453

The tea rooms are situated in the courtyard of Temple Newsam House, one of the most visited historic houses in Leeds. Another local attraction is Home Farm, which is within easy travelling distance of the tea room.
The specialities at the Temple Newsam Tea Room are the home baked cakes and biscuits and Earl Grey is the speciality tea.

OULTON

De Vere Oulton Hall

Rothwell Lane   Disabled Access
Oulton   Parking on site
01532 821000

The Grade II listed building is set in exquisite historical gardens designed by Humphrey Repton. Built in Ashlar stone in a classical style, it has wide tripartite windows, an entrance portico with ornate Ionic capitals or fluted columns and fine carved over door panelling.
Afternoon Tea serves assorted finger sandwiches, a scone with jam and clotted cream, fruit cake with Wensleydale cheese and a choice of pastries from the trolley. Cakes, scones and jams are home made and there is a wide range of teas including Earl Grey, Jasmine, Lapsang Souchong and Rosehip and Hibiscus herbal tea. Indian and iced teas are also available.

PATELEY BRIDGE

Yorkshire

Barbara's Tea Rooms

2 Park View   Disabled Access
Bridgehousegate   Parking outside
Pateley Bridge
Nr. Harrogate
01423 711013

Situated opposite the garage and convenient for walking, fishing and sightseeing the Yorkshire Dales, Barbara's Tea Rooms are set in an unusual building, serving a range of home made cakes, scones and jams.
Afternoon Tea offers a choice of sandwich with scone, jam and cream, cake and tea or coffee. There is an assortment of gateaux, fruit pies and cheesecakes and a baked egg custard pie. Teas include Ceylon, Darjeeling and Earl Grey.

PONTEFRACT

Pomfret Tea Rooms

16 Salter Row   Parking 50m.
Pontefract
01977 707957

With a town centre position, Pomfret Tea Rooms is close to the race course, the castle and the Buttercross.
Inside, the decor is Victorian and guests enjoy waitress service. A typical tea consists of a toasted sandwich with lemon meringue pie and tea or coffee. There is a selection of home made desserts and a wide range of filter coffees. Fruit teas by Ashbys offer an alternative to traditional China and Earl Grey.

Closed: Sundays.

The White House

Anvil Square   Disabled Access
Reeth   Parking 50m.
Nr. Richmond
01748 884763

Close to the countryside and many local crafts, The White House offers good views and pleasant decor, enhanced by fine bone china at table. There is no set menu, but the variety of cakes, scones and jams are home made, and sandwiches are served with a huge salad. Assam, Darjeeling and Earl Grey are the traditional teas on offer, and there is also a selection of herbal teas.

Closed: Wednesdays and Thursdays; Tuesdays also between January and Easter; and closed for whole of February.

ROSEDALE ABBEY

Abbey Tea Room

Abbey Stores and Tearoom   Disabled Access
Rosedale Abbey   Parking 50m.
Nr. Pickering
01751 417475

The pretty blue and primrose Laura Ashley tea room has picture windows overlooking the village green. During the iron mining boom of the early 20th century the site was part of a large store, supplying everything from sacks of flour to clothing.
Yorkshire Cream Tea serves a scone with strawberry jam, whipped cream, home made cake and a pot of tea. Abbey Special Tea comprises salmon and cucumber sandwiches, a scone and pot of tea. Sandwiches are freshly made and cakes and scones home baked. Ginger scone with ginger jam and cream or apricot and cheese gateau are just a couple of the mouthwatering choices on the menu. Teas include Ceylon, Darjeeling and Earl Grey.

Closed: End of October until Easter.

SHEFFIELD   Yorkshire

Tilly's Tearooms
655 Ecclesall Road
Sheffield
01742 687356

Disabled Access
Parking 50m

Tilly's Tearooms are situated on one of Sheffield's more exclusive shopping roads. A traditional tearoom, tablecloths, soft music and tasteful decor contribute to its quaint image. Proprietor Julie Roe makes every effort to give a friendly and efficient service in a relaxing environment.

Afternoon Tea serves a home baked scone with jam and fresh cream and a pot of Yorkshire tea or cup of house coffee. There is a choice of various home made cakes and speciality coffees. Teas such as Camomile, Darjeeling Earl Grey, Mango, Orange Pekoe and Passion Fruit are stocked for the more discerning palate.

SKIPTON

Hemingway's The Tea Shop
10A-11A Craven Court
Skipton
01756 798035

Disabled Access
Parking 100m.

Situated in the Victorian Craven Court, Hemingway's combines the excellence of home made cooking and traditional service to its patrons, its boast being that it is the only place in Skipton which sells a wide range of Taylors coffee beans, teas and home made jams and preserves.

Visitors taking afternoon tea can relax to the popular resident pianist. They can also enjoy the home made foods. Owners Tim and Anne Hemingway highly recommend the ever popular gateaux, fresh cream meringues and hot chocolate fudge cake. Teas available include Assam, Ceylon, China, Darjeeling and Earl Grey.

Closed: Sundays.

SLAITHWAITE   **Yorkshire**

Moonraker Floating Tea Room
Commercial Mills   Parking on site
Slaithwaite
Nr. Huddersfield
01484 846370

Moonraker Tea Room has a distinctive location on board a narrow boat, on
the canal between locks 23 and 24. The boat is fitted out in pine, creating a
warm, clean atmosphere. Central heating runs through well-polished copper
pipes and on display are various brass fittings with traditional painted pots
and plates, some of which are for sale.

Cakes and scones are baked in the galley daily, and there is no set menu for
afternoon tea, so there are plenty of options. Among the teas are Ceylon
Orange Pekoe, Darjeeling and Earl Grey, with herbal teas Rosehip,
Blackcurrant or Camomile.

Closed: Mondays (except Bank Holidays).

TERRINGTON

Flat Top Tea Rooms
Flat Top House   Disabled Access
Terrington   Parking on site
01653 648427

Local to Castle Howard and various footpaths for keen walkers and cyclists,
Flat Top Tea Rooms are housed in converted farm buildings with a courtyard
entrance. The decor is olde worlde, with a blue and cream theme. Clothes
airers, pine dressers and lots of china give an authentic feel. Proprietors June
and Kay Gill are happy to welcome coach parties, although notice is
appreciated.

Afternoon Tea comprises a round of sandwiches with a scone, jam and cream,
a piece of home made cake and a pot of tea. Scones, cakes, pies and jams are
all home baked and Earl Grey is the favourite tea in the pot.

Closed: Mondays.

THORNE   **Yorkshire**

The Gates Tea Room
29 King Street
Thorne
Nr. Doncaster
01405 813634

Disabled Access
Parking on site

The Gates Tea Rooms were built in 1700 as the original gate house for carts entering Thorne. After that the building was a beer house, stonemason's and cobbler's. Dark wood tables and chairs complement the wooden beams inside to give the impression of bygone ages. The conservatory or the tea garden at the rear are ideal for the summer.

Cream Teas are served by a friendly staff and there is no set menu, but a variety of home baked pies, biscuits, cakes and scones, which includes specialities like chocolate cake, buns and mince pies. The favourite tea on offer is Earl Grey.

Closed: Bank Holiday Mondays.

THORNTON

Ann's Peacock Tearoom
New Farm
Thornton
Nr. Bradford
01274 833214

Disabled Access
Parking on site

Thornton was the birthplace of the Bronte sisters and is within easy reach of Haworth where they wrote their masterpieces. Ann's Peacock Tearoom is in the farmhouse dining room and has a stone fireplace, with a relief carving of a stag hunt, from the local castle which was demolished in 1961. Christopher and Ann Foster are the proprietors who offer home made cakes and scones baked by Anne in the farmhouse kitchen. A splendid tea consists of ham and eggs with mushrooms and tomatoes, pineapple teabread and butter, cakes and scones and free refills of tea. Among the teas are Assam, Ceylon, China, Darjeeling and Earl Grey.

Closed: Weekdays, and between December and February.

Val's Tea Shop

61 Kirkgate   Disabled Access
Wakefield   Parking 50m.
01924 378996

Opposite Ridings Shopping Centre and close to the cinema, Val's Tea Shop
revels in old world decor and smart, traditionally dressed waiting staff.
Cream Tea serves a pot of tea with scones, strawberry preserve and fresh
cream and there is a good choice of cakes, desserts and ice cream, with cakes,
scones and jams being home made. Among the teas are Assam, Ceylon, China,
Darjeeling and Earl Grey.

Closed: Sundays.

YORK

Betty's Cafe Tea Rooms

6-8 St. Helen's Square   Disabled Access
York
01904 659142

Betty's Cafe Tea Rooms were opened in 1937 and designed to match the interior
of The Queen Mary liner. During World War Two it was a famous rendezvous
for Canadian and RAF airmen. Downstairs is a mirror with names etched on
by those airmen, which is today visited by their relatives.
Cream Tea offers two sultana scones with butter, whipped cream and preserve
and a pot of tearoom blend tea. Bread, cakes, scones and jams are all made at
Betty's own bakery and specialities include Yorkshire Fat Rascals, Yorkshire
Curd Tart and Swiss Rosti. St. Helena coffee is exclusive to Betty's from the
island of St. Helena. Teas include Assam, Ceylon, China, Darjeeling and Earl
Grey.

The Earl Grey Tearooms

13-14 The Shambles   Disabled Access
York   Parking 100m.
01904 654353

The Shambles is one of the oldest streets in North Europe, dating back to
1086. It is close to York Minster, the Jorvik Viking Centre and York's museums.
Still featuring some of the original wooden beams, The Earl Grey Tearooms
has wooden chairs and all the tables are covered with lace tablecloths. Guests
have the choice of Smoking or Non-Smoking rooms and are waited on by
traditionally dressed waiters and waitresses.
Cream Tea comprises scones with whipped cream and preserve with a pot of
tea. High Tea offers a choice of sandwich, scone, jam and cream or a fresh
cream cake with a pot of tea. Twelve different teas feature on the menu.

The National Trust Treasurer's House

Minster Yard   Parking 100m.
York
01904 624247

Tucked away inside the historic Treasurer's House behind York Minster, the
tea room provides an oasis of peace in the heart of a busy city.
A typical Tea might comprise prawn mayonnaise sandwich, with salad garnish,
a piece of cake from the selection and a pot of tea. Cakes and scones are home
baked and include Yorkshire specialities. Child sized portions are available.
There is a range of herbal and fruit teas with Assam, Ceylon, Darjeeling and
Earl Grey as the traditional teas in the pot.

Closed: 1st November to 1st April.

York Tea Room

30 Goodramgate
York

Disabled Access
Parking 100m.

01904 659282

Guests receive a warm Yorkshire welcome to the York Tea Room, a 13th Century listed building with access to the National Trust shop.

There is no set Tea menu. Freshly prepared food is of a high quality, using ingredients from local suppliers. Cakes, scones and puddings are home baked on the premises and many are local dishes. Ice creams and mineral waters are also supplied locally, and teas include the Yorkshire blend, Assam, Darjeeling and Earl Grey as well as fruit teas Peach, Passion Fruit and Blackcurrant.

Closed: Sundays.

-------0-------

Thank God for tea!
What would the world do without tea?
How did it exist?
I am glad that I was not born before tea.

(Sydney Smith, 1771-1845)

In Endymion, I leaped headlong into the sea,
and thereby have become better acquainted with
the surroundings, the quicksands, and the rocks,
than if I had stayed upon the green shore,
and piped a silly pipe,
and took tea and comfortable advice.

(John Keats)

SCOTLAND

THE POETS AT TEA
(MACAULAY)

The cosy fire is bright and gay,
The merry kettle boils away
And hums a cheerful song.
I sing the saucer and the cup;
Pray, Mary, fill the teapot up,
and do not make it strong.

Barry Pain
1864-1928

NEW ABBEY

Abbey Cottage
26 Main Street
New Abbey
01387 850377

Disabled Access
Parking 50m.

Beside the romantic, historic ruin of Sweetheart Abbey, Abbey Cottage is tastefully furnished in Laura Ashley, with pastel tablecloths. Intricate samplers cover the walls, sewn by proprietor Morag McKie and her daughters. Healthy, delicious food is served in a Non-Smoking atmosphere and free range eggs are used in the cooking, much of which is done by Jacqui Wilson, Morag's daughter and fellow proprietor.

There is no set menu, but cakes, gingerbread, shortbread and fruit loaves offer a tempting selection, with carrot cake highly recommended and the jams full of home grown fruit. Assam, Ceylon, Darjeeling and Earl Grey are the teas in the pot.

Closed: January to March inclusive and weekdays in November and December.

WIGTOWN

Wayside Tearoom
2 Agnew Crescent
Wigtown
01988 402333

Disabled Access
Parking 100m.

Wayside Tearoom is a good place to stop and rest between visits. Decorated in relaxing shades of cream and green with pine woodwork, the colour scheme provides a natural background for a display of seasonal hanging houseplants. On one wall there is a huge twelve foot by six foot Ordnance Survey Map of the area for the benefit of touring customers.

All baking is done on the premises by proprietors Marion Bell and Malcolm Smith. There is a choice of about thirty scones, tray bakes and sponges and a large selection of Twinings Fruit and Herbal teas in addition to the old favourites Assam, Darjeeling and Earl Grey.

The Hayloft Tearoom

Back Wynd   Parking 50m.
Falkland
01337 857590

Not far from Falkland Palace, The Hayloft Tearoom is a converted Hayloft, hence the name. Bright and cheerful, it is situated on the first floor and boasts a friendly, personal service.

Cakes and scones are home baked and though large parties can request fixed menus, the most popular items are individually priced. Scones, fruit slice, carrot cake, butterscotch cake and chocolate cake are firm favourites and there is a choice of Darjeeling and Earl Grey to wash them down.

Closed: Thursdays. End of October to April (except weekends in March).

Kind Kyttock's Kitchen

Cross Wynd   Disabled Access
Falkland   Parking opposite
01337 857477

Situated opposite the village green in the centre of the village, Kind Kyttock's Kitchen is named after the heroine in Dunbar's poem, who provided hospitality for weary travellers. Part of the building dates back to 1712, some of the original features having been retained to give atmosphere to the tea room.

Afternoon Tea offers a choice of two scones or two Scot's pancakes, or one of each with butter and jam, followed by two home made cakes and a cup of tea. Proprietor Bert Dalrymple endeavours to produce everything from the tea room itself, maintaining high standards by using only the best ingredients. Home made bread, cakes, scones and jams have a better flavour which cannot be matched by items bought in. Among the teas are Assam, Ceylon, China, Darjeeling and Earl Grey.

Closed: Mondays.

DINGWALL Highlands

DINGWALL   **Highlands**

The Station Tea Room and Craft Shop

Station Square   Disabled Access
Dingwall   Parking on site
01349 865894

Part of Dingwall Railway Station, the Tea Room and Craft Shop is an apt welcome to the attractive small market town which offers a good range of shops to its visitors. The Station itself is a listed building, built in 1886 for the Highland Railway. About half the building, including the former waiting rooms, have been transformed into an attractive tea room and quality gift shop, which sells many items made by local craftspeople.

The local baker bakes the bread, but cakes, scones and jams are all home made. Afternoon Tea serves a pot of tea with a scone, jam and butter. Freshly brewed teas include Assam, Ceylon, China, Darjeeling and Earl Grey.

Closed: Sundays.

ELPHIN

Elphin Tea Room

Elphin   Disabled Access
01854 666214   Parking on site

North of Ullapool and close to lochs, castles and distilleries, the location boasts the finest views in Scotland, with seven mountains visible from the car park. There is no set menu, but there is a good variety of individually home baked items. Everything is home made and supplied by proprietors Nicholas and Lorraine Brooks with a tempting array of special goodies from gingerbread to cheesecakes and gateaux, though the choice is too numerous to list.

Closed: November to Easter.

Sir Walter Scott's Traditional Tearoom

Romanes and Paterson   Disabled Access
62 Princes Street
Edinburgh
0131 225 4966

Nestling on the second floor of this well-known Edinburgh store lies the delightful Sir Walter Scott's Traditional Tearoom. With panoramic views of Princes Street, the Castle and surrounding gardens, this tearoom is deservedly popular. Tastefully decorated with fresh flowers on the tables and a friendly service.

Tea is served to include a freshly cut sandwich, scone with butter and jam, a choice of traybake and tea or coffee. Bread, cakes, scones and jams are all home made, with carrot cake, caramel shortbread and traybakes as the favourites. Assam, Ceylon and Darjeeling feature among the teas.

DAVIDSON'S MAINS

The Village Tea Room

55 Quality Street   Disabled Access
Davidson's Mains   Parking 50m.
Nr. Edinburgh
0131 312 7654

This Non-Smoking tea room is set in the middle of the village at the roundabout and within visiting distance of Cramond Foreshore and Lauriston Castle. To the rear there is a courtyard patio totally enclosed which proves popular in summer.

There is no set menu, but scones and cakes are well-priced and all home baked, and from the dining area it is possible to see into the spotless kitchen where they are made. Bread and jams are also home made and there is a choice of teas including Assam, Ceylon, China, Darjeeling and Earl Grey.

Closed: Sundays.

The Jenny Traditional Tea Rooms and Restaurant

18-20 Royal Exchange Square   Disabled Access
Glasgow   Parking 50m.
0141 204 4988

Two minutes from George Square in the historical centre of Glasgow, this traditional Victorian Tea Room is reminiscent of Glasgow's once famous tea rooms. Situated in the square that it will share with the Gallery of Modern Art from 1996, The Jenny boasts floral curtains, wallpaper and tablecloths with wooden furniture and old fireplaces and is divided up into five areas to make the atmosphere still more homely.

Jenny Afternoon Tea serves sandwiches, a scone with butter and jam, cake and tea. Cakes and scones are home baked, and among the specialities are the large brioche buns made to The Jenny's own recipe and home made fudge. There is a wide range of teas including Assam, Ceylon, China, Darjeeling and Earl Grey.

The Willow Tea Room

217 Sauchiehall Street   Parking 50m.
Glasgow
0141 332 0521

Situated above Henderson the jeweller in the precinct The Willow Tea Room was designed by internationally acclaimed architect Charles Rennie Mackintosh in 1904 as a tea room. Closing in 1926, it was put to several other uses before being restored to its original design in 1983 by the current owner and enjoys an international reputation as a "must see" on any visit to Glasgow. The silver furniture is a particularly interesting feature.

Afternoon Tea comprises sandwiches, scones and cake or pastries, or there are many cakes, desserts and ice creams to choose from. Fourteen varieties of coffee and twenty seven of tea ensure that no one goes away feeling thirsty.

Closed: Sundays and public holidays.

The Tudor Tearoom
5 Harling Drive   Disabled Access
Troon   Parking on site
01292 318448

The Tudor Tea Room was originally converted from a golf-club maker's workshop and overlooks three of Troon's well-known public golf courses through the bay windows.

Tea at the Tudor comprises a round of sandwiches of the customer's choice, a scone, pancake or potato scone, and a cake from the display. Cakes, scones and pancakes are home made and there is a good selection to choose from.

-------0-------

It frequently breakfasts at five-o'clock tea,
and dines on the following day.

(Lewis Carroll)

ALYTH

Tayside

The Singing Kettle
14 Airlie Street
Alyth
Nr. Blairgowrie
01828 632426

Disabled Access
Parking on site

The Singing Kettle whistles for attention just before visitors reach the Square and with its Indian Tree tableware, the pink walls featuring a double white alcove, and the corniced ceiling which draws regular admiration from guests, it is well worth a visit.

Cakes and scones are home baked, with a sumptuous choice including carrot cake, cream meringues, Rocky Road slice and Mississippi mud pie. Among the teas are Assam, Darjeeling and Earl Grey.

Closed: Half day Wednesdays and Half day Sundays.

ARBROATH

Calum's Tearoom
21 Commerce Street
Arbroath
01241 431229

Disabled Access
Parking 50m.

Calum's Tearooms are "like tea rooms used to be" in the words of proprietors Benita O'Reilly and James McLean. Elegantly designed menus reminiscent of the 1920s complement the peach wallpaper and matching tablecloths. The flowered china and grandfather's clock combine to make a tea room where regulars and visitors return again and again. Glen Miller music plays quietly in the background or the pianist plays Gershwin classics, while waitresses in traditional uniforms bring the home made food to the tables.

Cakes and scones are baked on the premises and are washed down by a choice of seven coffees or fifteen teas, including Assam, Ceylon, China, Darjeeling and Earl Grey.

Closed: Sundays between April and September.

The Cottage Gallery/Jane's Kitchen

Dundee Road
Newtyle
Nr. Blairgowrie
01828 650204

Disabled Access
Parking on site

Five miles from the Glamis Castle walk to the local folly, the tea room is set in an old farmhouse kitchen with a stone floor and log fire. To add to the atmosphere there is a low ceiling and old kitchen cupboards display local pottery and handmade goods. The gallery is through a short passage, where local artists exhibit their work.

Teas are served in the old cottage garden during the summer. Guests help themselves from the selection of home made cakes, scones and jams on the counter, whilst teas, coffees and soft drinks are brought to the table, including Assam and Earl Grey.

Closed: Mondays all year; weekdays in January.

-------0-------

A hardened and shameless tea-drinker, who has for twenty years diluted his meals with only the infusion of this fascinating plant, whose kettle has scarcely time to cool; who with tea amuses the evening, with tea solaces the midnight and with tea welcomes the morning.

(Samuel Johnson - Review in the Literary Magazine, 1757)

WALES

THE POETS AT TEA
(Wordsworth)

"Come, little cottage girl, you seem
To want my cup of tea;
And will you take a little cream?
Now tell the truth to me."
She had a rustic, woodland grin
Her cheek was soft as silk,
And she replied, "Sir, please put in
A little drop of milk."

Barry Pain
1864-1928

Bronant Tea Rooms

Ty Nant
Nr. Corwen
01490 460344

Disabled Access
Parking on site

Halfway between Llangollen and Betws-y-Coed, the Bronant tea rooms are close to Snowdonia National Park, Bala Lake and the Denbigh Moors. A former sixteenth century coach house, the beamed ceiling gives a historic feel to the venue which incorporates a gift shop.

Welsh Cream Tea offers a scone with jam, cream and a pot of tea. Welsh Tea serves bara brith plus a scone with jam and a pot of tea. Bread, cakes and scones are all home baked and specialities include Welsh Cakes, and Rarebit. There is a good selection of teas, including Assam, Ceylon, China, Darjeeling and Earl Grey.

Closed: Wednesdays and Thursdays half day closing; throughout November to mid-February.

ST ASAPH

Turners Tea Room

1 Mount Road
St. Asaph
01745 583097

Disabled Access
Parking 100m.

Turners Tea Room is a vocational training unit run by Pengwern Hall, Rhuddlan, instructing young people with learning difficulties in the basic vocational and social skills they require when they leave college.

Pine tables and chairs match the clean simplicity of the pine-clad walls and the country elegance of the pine dressers that display the teas and wholefoods for sale. Terracotta tiled floors add to the atmosphere of the listed building that was once a post office.

Tea brings a round of sandwiches, a scone with jam and cream and a pot of tea. Cakes and scones are home made and include carrot cake and Victoria sandwich. Among the teas are Assam and Earl Grey.

Pip's Traditional Tea Rooms

56 Chester Street   Disabled Access

Wrexham   Parking 100m.

01978 312312

The building dates from 1543 and is situated opposite Henblas Street near to the Wynnstay Hotel and not far from local attractions such as St. Giles Church. The interior is adorned with the work of local artists in addition to which there are gifts and various crafted items on sale, from sugar craft to floral displays. Waitresses wear traditional costume and there is absolutely No Smoking, with a health policy which is reflected in the food.

Afternoon Welsh Tea constitutes a pot of tea with a choice of sandwich, brown or white bread, a scone, jam and cream and is very reasonably priced. Bread, cakes, scones and jams are home made, and there are speciality traditional puddings to indulge in whilst enjoying the friendly atmosphere. Teas include Assam, Ceylon, China, Darjeeling and Earl Grey as well as thirty five herbal teas.

Closed: Some Sundays.

-------0-------

We had a kettle: we let it leak:
Our not repairing it made it worse.
We haven't had any tea for a week...
The bottom is out of the Universe!

(Rudyard Kipling)

CENARTH

Cenarth Tearooms and Slate Shop
"Crymant"   Parking 50m.
Cenarth
01239 711213

Situated next to the National Coracle Centre with its 17th century water mill, Cenarth Tearooms are about fifty metres from the famous salmon leap waterfalls, the home of the coracle fishermen and renowned worldwide for their outstanding beauty. Cenarth itself is a conservation village with many fine walks around the local nature and history. The Tearooms are on two levels, with a model village and historic pictures in the basement. Tables and chairs are in matching dark wood and there are flowers on all the tables, with waiting service inside and in the garden, which is used seasonally.

Welsh Tea comprises a pot of tea, a scone with butter, jam and fresh cream from a local farm, and bara brith with butter. Cream Tea serves a pot of tea, a scone with butter, jam and fresh cream. Prices are very reasonable and cakes are all home baked. Teas include Assam, Darjeeling, Earl Grey and Lemon.

Closed: Weekdays in November and December.

MANORBIER

The Tearoom
Manorbier Garden Centre   Parking on site
Manorbier
Nr. Tenby
01834 87178

Close to the castle, beach and historic village, The Tearoom offers a range of gifts to its guests as well as home made rolls, cakes and scones.

Cream Tea consists of two scones, jam and cream, in addition to which there is a wonderful selection of fruit pies, cakes, with speciality being carrot, and pavlovas. Among the teas are Assam, Ceylon, Earl Grey and various herbal infusions.

STEPASIDE Dyfed

The Bothy Tea Rooms
Colby Woodland Gardens   Disabled Access
Stepaside   Parking on site
Nr. Narberth
01834 814163

Situated in a converted stable on National Trust property, The Bothy Tea Rooms are set in eight acres of woodland garden with an excellent collection of rhododendron and azalea.

All cakes and scones are home baked and there is a selection of delicious cakes, cream teas and local dairy ice cream sundaes. Among the teas are Assam, Ceylon, China and Earl Grey.

Closed: Beginning of November to beginning of April.

TENBY

Bramley's Tearoom
Plough Penny Field Nursery   Disabled Access
Nr. Tenby   Parking on site

Set in a beautiful village in the heart of South Pembrokeshire about four miles from Tenby, the tea room run by Liz Hainsworth Catering is set in a new Scandinavian style log cabin with a delightful Non-Smoking ambience, where quality, customer care and friendliness are bywords. Guests can sit outside in the small garden or on the verandah in warm weather.

Tea consists of a choice of sandwiches, a slice of teabread or fruitcake, scone with jam and cream and tea. Bread, cakes and scones are home made and proprietor Liz Hainsworth recommends her pastry. Teas include Assam and Earl Grey.

Closed: Mondays to Thursdays, October 31st to March 1st.

Celtic Fare Tea Rooms

Vernon House
St. Julian Street
Tenby

01834 845258

Disabled Access
Parking 50m.

Located just off Tudor Square on the way to the harbour, Celtic Fare Tea Rooms are part of the seaside town with its historic walls, castle and beautiful beaches.

The old fashioned interior is charming with its wooden floors, beams hung with jugs and teapots and authentic gas lamps in season which complement the fire burning in the Victorian hearth.

Fresh flowers and soothing Welsh music create the impression of a more gracious age, as do the splendid selection of home baked cakes, puddings and pastries. Rich, tangy lemon torte, banana or apple cake and pecan pie vie with the Welsh cakes, served hot from the griddle and scones with fruity jam and thick Caldey Island clotted cream. There is a variety of teas including Assam, Ceylon, China, Darjeeling and Earl Grey.

-------0-------

Lobster Mayonnaise Sandwich

Shred the lobster meat. Pour the mayonnaise over, add the yolks of three eggs and stir. Add half a teaspoon of salt, a little cayenne and white pepper, a pinch of nutmeg, half a mustard spoon, half a teaspoon of lemon juice, three drops of tarragon vinegar and a teaspoon of anchovy sauce.

(Five O' Clock Tea, 1886)

St. Mary's Tearooms

5 St. Mary's Street
Chepstow
01291 621711

Disabled Access
Parking 50m.

Proprietors Michael and Linda Johns try to give everyone personal service in the attractively decorated tea room. Otherwise there is waitress service for visitors who can sit outside in the cobbled street or in the courtyard to the rear in warm weather.

Cream Tea comprises two scones with jam, butter, clotted cream and a pot of tea. Specialities include the locally made farm ice creams from the Wye Valley, as well as a range of coffees from around the world and teas such as Assam, Ceylon, China, Darjeeling and Earl Grey.

Closed: Sundays from September to June.

GARN-YR-ERW

The Bara Brith Cafe/Tearoom

Garn Road
Garn-yr-Erw
Nr. Blaenavon
01495 792299

Parking on site

This cottage style tea room was once the old co-op and is set in the small mining village of Garn-Yr-Erw near to the Big Pit Mining Museum, steam trains and fishing lakes. The original marble bacon counter is still in use a hundred years on, exposed beams, checkered tablecloths, old family photographs and wall-mounted candlesticks give a sense of atmosphere and there is an old piano for customers to use, as well as a resident psychic offering palmistry and other such services.

Welsh Tea comprises a pot of tea with Welsh cakes, bara brith and sandwiches. Cakes, scones and jams are home baked and teas on offer are Darjeeling, Earl Grey and various herbal infusions.

Closed: weekends between October and Easter.

ABERSOCH

Gwynedd

Oriel Fach Cafe
High Street
Abersoch
01758 713158

Disabled Access
Parking 50m.

Abersoch is the "riviera of the Llyn peninsula", famous for water sports, a stunning coastline, walking and golfing. Oriel Fach Cafe is in the middle of the High Street. Antique furniture with period teapots and accessories show the original pictures, art prints and antiques for sale at their best.
Welsh Cream Tea serves a scone with jam, fresh cream and bara brith with a pot of tea. Cakes, scones and bara brith are home baked and teas include Darjeeling and Earl Grey.

Closed: Weekends between October and Easter.

BEAUMARIS

Spinning Wheel Tearooms
1 Bulkeley Place
Beaumaris
Anglesey
01248 810338

Parking 50m.

Spinning Wheel Tearooms are in a Grade II listed Georgian building and are not to be missed on a visit to Anglesey. Inside the bright, airy, clean decor are a selection of gifts, sweets and postcards as well as an ice cream parlour serving Denbigh Farmhouse ice cream at the entrance.
Waitresses bring Welsh Cream Tea, which comprises brown bread and butter, bara brith, Welsh cake and scone with jam and cream and a pot of tea. Spinning Wheel Afternoon Tea offers a choice of freshly made sandwich, bara brith, Welsh cake, scone with jam and fresh cream and a pot of tea. Bread, cakes and scones are home baked on the premises daily and high quality coffees and loose leaf teas wash the meal down, among them Darjeeling, Earl Grey and English Breakfast.

Closed: January.

CONWY

Anna's Tea Rooms
9 Castle Street   Parking 100m.
Conwy
01492 580908

Set above Conwy's Outdoor Shop, Anna's Tea Rooms are within easy reach of the castle. Anna's Afternoon Tea offers a round fresh sandwiches, two slices of bara brith and a pot of Anna's Tea. Cream Tea constitutes two home made fruit scones, jam, cream and the pot of tea. Bread, cakes and scones are all home baked, with bara brith being a popular speciality. There is a good selection of teas, including Assam, Ceylon, China, Darjeeling and Earl Grey.

DINAS MAWDDWY

The Station Coffee Shop
Dinas Mawddwy   Parking on site
Nr. Machnylleth
01650 531338

The Old Station Coffee Shop is on the right of the entrance to Meirion Mill and was originally the waiting room and booking hall of the Mawddwy Railway, which took passengers and slate seven miles down the Dyfi Valley. The location boasts wonderful scenery and there is seating outside on fine days.
There is no set menu, but customers can help themselves from the buffet style counter to individually priced items. Bread, cakes and scones are home baked and there is a wide choice of cakes, chutneys, jams, honey, fudge, chocolate and ice creams to enjoy on site or to take home. There is a selection of herbal and fruit teas in addition to the traditional favourites Assam, Ceylon, China, Darjeeling and Earl Grey.

Closed: Mid-November to March.

Market Hall Tea and Coffee Rooms
College Green   Parking 100m.
Tywyn
01654 710733

Set in the only Market Hall, a hundred year old building in Tywyn, near to the Tall-y-Llyn Railway and Cader Iris, Market Hall Tea and Coffee Rooms have separate rooms available for smokers and non-smokers.
Cakes and scones are home baked and there is a choice of tea and coffee.

Closed: Sundays, and half days on Mondays and Wednesdays.

-------0-------

Tea, Please

I've taken tea on Bahrain's isle,
Sri Lanka and Hong-Kong,
Where desert sands run mile on mile
And sunlight's powerful strong;
Tea from the galley in our plane
Gave ease when flights were long.
In tropic heat, in freezing rain
The tea-cup came along.

Tea in Japan, tea in Malay,
Tea in Aden's heat.
At cricket on a summer's day
A tea is hard to beat.
And I remember taking tea in the land of Lorna Doone
With Devon cream - just you and me
Whilst on our honeymoon.

(Jasper Miles, 1994)

The Copper Kettle

103 The Struet   Disabled Access

Brecon   Parking 100m.

01874 611349 / 754848

Situated between Boots and Kwik Save, the olde worlde tea and coffee shop is ideally situated for weary walkers and visitors to the Brecon Beacons. Inside it has oak beams, and displays prints by local and internationally known artists in the coffee lounge.

There is no set menu, but there is a good variety of well-priced scones, and other specialities of the house are the continental gateaux. Bread, cakes, scones and jams are all home made and the teas include China, Darjeeling and Earl Grey.

LLYSWEN

The Copper Kettle

The Village Green   Disabled Access

Llyswen   Parking 100m.

Nr. Brecon

01874 611349 / 754848

Situated in the centre of Llyswen, The Copper Kettle is well-placed for visitors to the Brecon Beacons and for fishing on the River Wye.

The attractive olde worlde cottage is a tea and coffee shop with oak beams, selling collectors prints as well as gifts and antiques.

There is no set menu, which allows for greater choice. Scone with jam and butter is available or a large toasted teacake. Bread, cakes, scones and jams are home made. Specialities include waffles served with maple syrup or black cherries and cream. Among the teas on offer are China, Darjeeling and Earl Grey.

Closed: Mondays.

The Drover's Rest Tea Rooms
Dol-y-Coed Road   Parking 50m.
Llanwrtyd Wells
01591 610264

The attractive 18th century tea room has been tastefully restored and is situated in the centre of this mid-Wales town, on the banks of the River Iflon, opposite the Green. It is an ideal place to take refreshment after pony trekking or mountain biking.

Welsh Afternoon Teas are made using traditional methods. Bread, cakes, scones and jams are all home made and the selection of teas include Assam, Ceylon, China, Darjeeling and Earl Grey.

NEWTOWN

Bank Cottage Tea Rooms
The Bank   Disabled Access
Newtown   Parking 50m.
01686 625771

Newtown is situated in the middle of Wales with the River Severn running through the town. Bank Cottage Tea Rooms is an oak framed 16th century building, which has been restored by the proprietors Derek and Audrey Davies to its original glory, featuring a log fire in winter and a wealth of wooden beams inside and out. Antique tables and chairs, period cutlery, Willow pattern tableware add to the traditional atmosphere.

Cream Tea consists of two scones, jam and real cream with a pot of tea. Welsh Tea constitutes two slices of wholemeal bread, two jams, a choice of cake and a pot of tea. Cakes, scones and jams are all home made and fruit for the pies and jams is home grown. Along with various fruit and herbal teas, Darjeeling and Earl Grey feature as the favourite drinks.

Closed: Sundays.

Old Mill Teashop

Felin Crewi   Disabled Access
Penegoes   Parking on site
Machnynlleth
01654 703113

Adjacent to a working water mill, two miles from the New Celtica Exhibition and four miles from the centre for Alternative Technology, the tea shop is situated in an oat kiln, where previous millers used to toast their oats before milling them. It extends into the old dairy and stable and overlooks the river so that in fine weather, guests can sit outside by the river and listen to the gentle swish of the water wheel.
Tea comprises a white or wholemeal scone with butter, jam and whipped cream, bara brith, Welsh cakes and a pot of tea. Cakes and scones are home baked, using stoneground flour from the mill. Teas include Assam, Ceylon, Darjeeling and Earl Grey.

Closed: Mondays in term time and from October to Easter.

RHAYADER

Carole's Cake Shop and Tearoom

South Street   Parking 50m.
Rhayader
01597 811060

Within easy reach of the Elan Valley Reservoirs and the Welsh crystal factory, Carole's Cake Shop and Tearoom is set in the town centre. Cream Tea provides a pot of tea, home made scones, jam and cream. Welsh Tea constitutes a pot of tea, bread and butter with honey, a scone with jam, Welsh cakes and bara brith.
Cakes, scones and jams are all home made, the most popular being the carrot cake, bara brith and Welsh cakes. Among the teas are Assam, Ceylon, China, Darjeeling and Earl Grey.

Closed: Thursday afternoons; beginning of week during January and February.

The Cottage Creamery
Rhossili
Gower
Swansea
01792 391355

Disabled Access
Parking 50m.

The Cottage Creamery is set on a superb beach with excellent bathing and spectacular scenery, in a village historically notorious for smuggling and wrecking. Gower was the first place to be set aside as an area of outstanding natural beauty. The village of Rhossili is situated on a two hundred foot cliff face which leads to the magnificent Worm's Head Island.

Clotted cream teas are reasonably priced, with cakes all home baked. Specialities include Welsh Dairy ice cream, bara brith and Welsh cakes. Among the teas are Assam, Ceylon, China, Darjeeling and Earl Grey.

Closed: Autumn to Easter except for fine weekends.

-------0-------

Samson

Mix one bottle of Claret, one of champagne, two of soda water and a wine glass of sherry. Add 6 strawberries and 4 tablespoons of sifted sugar.
Always add the sugar slowly, just before serving.

(Five O' Clock Tea, 1886)

YOU CAN HELP.........

In this first edition we cannot possibly cover every tea room. Because owners and staff change we may have omitted some of the best and possibly included some of the worst!

If you can tell us anything to add or deduct from the next edition please write and let us know, addressing your letter to:-

The Editor
Whitehill Publishing
7 Bournemouth Road
Chandlers Ford
Eastleigh
Hampshire
SO53 3DA